ANCIENT HEALING
IN A MODERN WORLD

KIT KARLYLE

First Printing 2019
First Edition 2019
10 9 8 7 6 5 4 3 2 1

ISBN: 978-1-7339160-0-4

DEDICATION

To my mother, Kit Wan Soo, who first introduced me to complementary and alternative medicine and world travel, and who healed herself naturally from kidney cancer. Her pioneering spirit paved a path in so many ways.

To Susan Ghadimi Navai, my second mom, whose wisdom, strength and grace are in my heart now and forever.

ACKNOWLEDGEMENTS

It is with great gratitude that I thank the people who have participated in my journey writing this book.

I begin with Ramin Omid, whose never-ending support, advice and friendship have been the cornerstone of completing this book. His 23-year expertise in the field of sleep medicine was the basis for the chapter dedicated to this subject.

To Natalie De Picciotto for being my supportive "Soul Sister" and safe harbor throughout this journey called life.

To Jesse Horowitz, friend, collaborator and comrade-in-arms who joined me in discovering many of the international locations in this book, and who continues to inspire me to further the journey.

To Wendy Vitalich and Nancy Solari for inspiring me by being examples of what's possible with determined focus and intention.

To Rati Godrej, my lifelong friend who has always been supportive of my health and wellness endeavors, and who first introduced me to authentic Ayurveda.

To Andrea Cegolon who helped me discover the riches of Northern Italy for "Benessere."

Special thanks to Richard Woods for sharing his kindness and knowledge which continues to inspire me.

To Andrew Lanz, Steve Pirato, Jeremy Bellotti, Anik Singal, and the entire team at LURN for their guidance and support.

To my editor Wayne Purdin whose insights and suggestions were invaluable.

To my book cover designer Faaizah Ali from Studio02.

Thanks to Heidi Woodworth, Diane Buckingham, Carsten Norgaard, Iris Schwartz, Shawn Chan, Susan Iida, Sandra Axelrod, and Sue B. for decades of friendship.

And to those not specifically mentioned, I send my gratitude for your energy and support.

.

TABLE OF CONTENTS

PREFACE

"Natural forces within us are the true healers of disease."
~Hippocrates (460-370 BC),
Greek physician, Father of Modern Medicine.

What did the world of health and wellness look like before modern medicine? What did ancient cultures do to combat disease and promote wellness in times before clinical breakthroughs? Where can these wisdoms be found? Do they still work? What can one do at home to recreate what worked back then? How many cultures still apply home remedies? What are the secrets handed down through generations to make us feel better? Where do our body's natural healing instincts and knowledge lie hidden? How can we awaken them? How do we find enough quiet wisdom within ourselves to hear them?

Over 14 years ago, I began a journey of discovery to answer these questions.

After experiencing many cultural healing methods around the world, I see how they are all based on Hippocrates' idea of Natural healing.

Mind you, there's ample room for all kinds of modalities and methods to heal. Modern medicine has saved and continues to save lives. Most of my international wellness experiences were with methods available before modern medicine as we know it, with two exceptions.

In Costa Rica, the Blue Zone philosophy for living was a recent subject of study, yet the application to our well-being is timeless. In the case of the United States, the study and science of sleep has revealed a wealth of information about this essential component of health that's often overlooked or ignored.

To be completely clear, I'm not a doctor. This book is written from the perspective of the ultimate patient. My penchant for extensive research has guided me on this journey. A professor friend of mine called me an "applied research scientist." No doubt this has proven true.

My research has revealed numerous preventative and healing methods. My form of research was to serve as a human "guinea pig," to see if what worked then still works now.

I immersed myself (sometimes quite literally) into the waters and realms of natural healing around the world.

After journeying tens of thousands of miles over 14 years in search of answers, I can now share my experience. With it, I also offer ways to simulate those healing experiences right where you are, right now.

And if you are already a world traveler, intrigued by world travel, or you are looking to begin an exploration for wellness, I provide interesting facts about each healing destination I visited as well.

INTRODUCTION
HEALTH - THE NEW CURRENCY

When the word *wealth* is brought up, what comes to mind? For many, the mental image that pops up immediately is money. Money to do, have, and see everything we want and to take care of those we love.

Now imagine for a moment that you had enough money; however, your health wasn't good. Low energy, sore joints, achy muscles, and diminished mobility could, no doubt, limit your enjoyment of life no matter how much money you had. Travel would become more difficult if not impossible, and activities would be restricted or cut short. How able are you to create and to share moments with your loved ones if you're limited by health issues?

Time and attention to well-being are as good as gold, the returns of which can be measured in the quality of life in our later years. Making such deposits starting now can create a significant difference in our lives and in the lives of loved ones far into the future.

HEALTHY AGING VS. SIMPLY GETTING OLDER

The passage of time is inevitable. Falling victim to it is not.

The typical symptoms of aging can be alleviated and, as I personally experienced, even reversed to some extent. Quite frankly, I was amazed by the effectiveness of some of the modalities I'll share with you.

Think about this. Have you noticed that, in general, the way you feel is the way you look? If you feel sluggish, achy, and sleep-deprived, there's a good chance that you'll look like it. If you have higher energy levels, less pain, and are well-rested, that bounce in your step can help you look 5 or even 10 years younger. So why not go for the latter, right?

We humans are all made of the same stuff, which hasn't changed much throughout our existence on earth. Therefore, it stands to reason that what helped the Romans and Greeks in 420 BCE, could have a good chance of working for us now in some capacity. However, each of us is different, and so is our "sweet spot" for wellness and feeling good daily.

Naturally, genetics, lifestyle, and daily activities can and will affect our bodies' ability to rejuvenate.

Stress is the number one culprit that causes premature aging, both physically, mentally and emotionally. Beings exist primarily in two states: Fight or Flight and Rest and Repair. Being able to manage stress through a daily practice has changed my life. But this didn't happen without first being taken down by stress-induced illness, a story I'll share with you shortly.

And because our bodies are designed to self-heal, assisting in any way possible can help us along the path of healthy aging.

Treating the symptom might make us feel better temporarily, but it doesn't necessarily heal the source of the affliction.

Symptoms are our bodies' way of telling us something is wrong. Listening to our bodies rather than masking this communication can ultimately help us to find a healing solution.

In today's world, old age isn't necessarily the cause of health issues. Surprisingly, research shows a spike in healthcare issues in the age group of 40-45 (Russell, 2006). In the U.S, I recently learned directly from a specialist that the age for recommended colonoscopies will be lowered to 45 from 50 because of an increase in cases in younger people.

It's never too early to start on the path to wellness.

Our bodies are with us from birth to death, enabling us to live and experience our world. Supporting our bodies to function optimally simply makes good sense.

Imagine for a moment what would happen to your car if you drove it every day for decades without changing the fluids, putting air in the tires, or doing any regular maintenance at all. Expecting it to operate optimally would be crazy.

Conversely, what would happen if you let your car sit for years without starting it? Most likely, the fluids would be dried up and the battery would be dead.

In essence, our cells are tiny batteries that are designed to keep us up and running with vitality. If they get low, a jumpstart might be required.

Through the ages, humans have sought ways to heal, to regenerate, and to rejuvenate long before modern medicine. Don't get me wrong; there's a real place for modern Western medicine. It can save and has saved lives. There's no discounting the importance of all forms of treatments available to us.

This book is about natural methods I've experienced that can help our bodies stay well, rejuvenate, and regenerate on their own, and that can add life to our years.

I call it a "Regeneration Jumpstart."

Remember, it's not our age that matters. Rather it is the quality of life we experience daily at any age that matters, and being healthy is the foundation of this quality.

The final chapter of this book will bring together my experiences and research to provide an action plan you can start today, a plan to enhance your well-being and ultimately the quality of your life.

Chapter 1

How Did It Start?

WORKAHOLIC.

I didn't know what workaholic even meant. I figured that everyone worked nonstop to achieve goals. Right? The danger begins when balance and clarity are lost, and the fear of failure pushes you to unrealistic limits. Fear can cause stress on so many levels. And the worst part is that, sometimes, it creeps up on us and takes residence in our lives without us realizing it.

Then the symptoms appear. Sleepless nights, endless worry, stomach pains, neck pains, back pains, loss of appetite. The list takes on a surreptitious life of its own.

I didn't even understand what stress was as I mindlessly chased the popular notion of "success."

From the outside, it looked like I had a "successful" life, complete with all the material trappings of outward "success." However, I had unknowingly chased *someone else's idea* of success.

How did this happen?

After years of introspection and journeys of self, I realized that I was always just trying to prove myself. My inner blueprint was that I wasn't good enough and I needed to earn my worth in some way.

Every deal on the table was a do-or-die situation for me, which would serve to define if I were "good enough." I was unaware of the stress I was putting on myself to perform. Or if I did know in some way, I was in total denial.

In my 30s, I ended up in the hospital twice. I even required surgery to stop a potentially life-threatening situation, which I thought was just a reaction to increased responsibility and incessant worry.

Being much younger, recovering from stressful situations seemed to come readily with only a little R&R or downtime. I didn't realize that stress was a silent adversary that was slowly undermining my health and well-being. I neither tuned in to nor became conscious of what was happening.

Sleepless nights, continued medical issues, and fatigue were simply things to "warrior through" so that I could succeed with the "next big thing" on my plate. I was running my engine at 60 miles per hour in first gear, oblivious to the damage accumulating inside my body caused by continued stress to prove myself.

CHAPTER 2

WHEN MEDICATION ISN'T ENOUGH

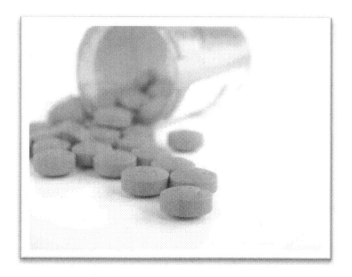

Whenever I had persistent aches and pains, the best way I knew how to handle it at the time was to take ibuprofen. It was convenient, quick, and effective. No doubt, this was a very Western way of living.

At first, I took it when I felt some sort of nagging pain. Then I started taking it every morning as a preventative measure. Yet, even with consistent dosing, the pains came back. Silencing the symptoms wasn't at all curing the cause, but I just didn't have the time nor inclination to listen. I also had no idea of the long-term effects of consistently medicating in this way. Simply put, I was "too busy."

Pain is our body's way of telling us that something is wrong and needs attention. Silencing those messages from our body is like not listening to a friend or family member when he or she is really hurting. I wouldn't think of doing that to anyone about whom I care deeply, yet I was doing it to my own body.

The statistics of self-medication in women are alarming. Perhaps it's a way of living up to being the Superwoman that everyone expects.

Women often subconsciously live out expectations of roles rather than their own authenticity and empowerment, and I was no different. I played the roles of wife, daughter, corporate executive, friend, and problem-solver with fervor, all the while believing that those were my identities.

After years of silencing the symptoms with pain killers, I came to realize that treating the cause might be a much more effective and sane path.

Where to start? That's when I went back to the research and learned about the natural solutions used by ancient cultures such as the Greeks and Romans since time immemorial.

I made a commitment to find and to experience natural wellness solutions. This commitment took me on a journey around the world, over a span of 14 years.

On that journey, I learned concepts and practices that helped me turn my life around and that can help you to do the same.

CHAPTER 3

BHUTAN

BREATH AND SILENCE IN THE HIMALAYAS

My discomfort with my current physical state grew ever-stronger alongside my willingness to keep medicating.

Something told me that I needed a break; not a temporary, get-your-mind-off-it break, but rather a true break from all that I knew and the way I was currently living.

So, instead of taking my usual scuba trip somewhere exotic, I chose a journey of introspection – a journey of finding myself.

I knew I couldn't do this alone. I mean, how do you find yourself when you don't have a clue where you are in the first place?

I knew that others trekked on journeys of self-discovery, so perhaps a trekking company could help. After multiple phone calls, I was referred to a 70-year-old guide who spoke perfect English. It came to light that he left the Western world at age 40 and found himself in Tibet looking for… himself. Perfect. Being guided by someone who has been where I wanted to be made sense. So, with resolve, I packed and boarded a plane to Bhutan to seek what was missing in my life. I later came to realize that what was missing was, simply, *me*.

Actually, when searching for distant lands, I initially didn't know where Bhutan was located. I just wanted to go somewhere extremely unfamiliar to do something extremely life-changing. My Type-A personality was still leading the charge, as it had always done.

I approached finding myself like another goal that needed to be accomplished. How counterintuitive is that? I asked my guide how I could find myself. He said to me, "Just be." What did that mean? So, I asked him, "What do I need to DO to just be?" He looked at me painfully and said nothing. I'm not certain to this day if, at that moment, he had any hope in my ability to quiet down and "just be."

After what seemed like hours of looking at me, he told me to say nothing and just walk. No questions and no conversation unless I needed medical attention. What I didn't know in that moment is that he wanted me to do this for what ended up being the longest 10 days in my life at the time. Alone with my just my thoughts and a couple of yaks, I was dumbfounded at the request. But, being my goal-driven self, I went with it.

Being a sea-level gal, trekking at high altitudes was challenging enough. The silence added to my physical discomfort. Plagued by the incessant chatter of my monkey mind, I trudged along the path, wondering what on earth I had gotten myself into. The cacophony of modern life seemed pretty good right about then. Hey, maybe finding myself wasn't all that important after all.

To boot, the journey was becoming more challenging. I couldn't breathe because I didn't know what real breathing meant.

My mind chatter was incessant, telling me I was bat-crazy to be flying across the world to hike around where I couldn't breathe just to find myself.

Then, after 10 days in sometimes painful silence, I ultimately remembered why I had gone to Bhutan. I was finally hearing for the first time what my body, my heart, and my soul were telling me.

And over that month spent high in the Himalayas, I learned how to breathe. I mean *really* breathe. Pacing my breathing also helped me to quiet the chatter in my mind.

My wise guide taught me techniques such as breath awareness and listening within that helped me to focus on what I had originally set out to discover.

These gifts of breathing and basic meditation opened an entirely new channel of awareness that was nothing shy of life-changing.

He also taught me some basic movements that he called "Tibetan Rites." He didn't know if they actually originated in Tibet, but the country of origin was ultimately unimportant. I stumbled on through as he patiently led the way. This was the first time I had experienced anything like yoga; he told me that he had practiced it for 30+ years. All I knew is that at 70-something, he could traverse gracefully at high altitudes like a man less than half his age. I was going with the program. Maybe it could help me too. More than ever, I could see how much I needed it.

When I returned home, the stressful pace of daily life to which I had been so accustomed was almost unbearable.

I then made a series of choices that dramatically altered the direction of my life. I had a new-found clarity regarding my life that I didn't know could exist for me.

And it started with the things I owned.

Simply looking at my closet caused me to feel overwhelmed. How on earth did I end up with so much *stuff*? I proceeded to give away almost all my clothes, shoes, and accessories – the trappings of excess in my past. One of my favorite humanitarian organizations, which helps formerly homeless women find jobs, could put them to good use. I realized that energetically, I needed to clear the space for new ways of just being.

I dove deeper into researching the meaning of health, wellness, and well-being, all while practicing the breathing and meditation techniques I learned in Bhutan as a complete newbie.

The beauty of breathing and meditation is that you can do it anywhere, and at any time. And if not now, when?

BREATHING

As simple and as automatic as it may seem, focusing on our breathing can make a big difference. When I couldn't breathe in the Himalayas, slowing down and breathing with intention helped me to keep going.

How many of us pay attention to our breath? Not many of us are conscious of our breathing patterns. Not many people, at least in the West, are taught to be aware of their breath, unless they're a musician, singer, dancer, athlete, yoga practitioner, or martial arts student. Without paying attention to our breath, the changes in breathing patterns that stress can cause also go unnoticed, and thus unmanaged. In the long run, poor breathing habits can take a toll on general health and well-being.

After all, it's the most basic way to fill our tanks with oxygen fuel. How funny would it be if we paid no attention to the gas or oil warning lights in our cars? It seems obvious that we need to, doesn't it?

Let's start with the benefits of mindful breathing.

When you've been upset or agitated you've probably heard someone tell you, "Just breathe."

Modern scientific evaluation of this ancient practice shows that slow and controlled breathing helps to calm your nervous system, reduce stress, and increase alertness (MacKinnon, 2016; Dalton, 2018).

Intentional breathing practices can also help reduce symptoms associated with insomnia, anxiety, depression, and post-traumatic stress disorder. Amazing benefits for such a simple action.

When we consciously send breath/oxygen to every part of the body including organs, we are subtly rejuvenating the body with focused energy. If you're experiencing pain, stiffness, or trouble in a certain area, focus breath with kindness into those areas. Our bodies do so much for us, and taking time to be present and nurturing through breath creates a positive environment for healing.

Breathing calmly and slowly tells your mind that everything is okay, that there's no saber-toothed tiger attempting to make you tonight's dinner. Conversely, rapid and short breaths indicate that danger might be around the corner, which creates a "fight or flight" response in our bodies.

Although a fight or flight response is very useful in certain rare circumstances (such as running from a wild animal), constantly being in this state can increase cortisol levels with possible serious negative effects. Of course, anything that we do consistently will have an effect – one way or another. More on this later.

Here are three basic breathing exercises you can start right where you are today.

COHERENT BREATHING

If you have the time to learn only one technique, this is the one to incorporate into your daily routine. In coherent breathing, the goal is to breathe at a rate of five breaths per minute, which basically translates into inhaling and exhaling to the count of six. If you've never practiced breathing exercises before, you may have to work up to this practice gradually, starting with slowly inhaling and exhaling to the count of three and working your way up to six.

1. Sitting upright or lying down, place your hands on your belly.

2. Slowly breathe in through your nose, expanding your belly, to the count of five.

3. Pause for two counts. Be present. Note what you are feeling.

4. Slowly breathe out through your nose to the count of five.

Consistency with this type of breathing can be a very useful tool in your toolbox for establishing the foundation of overall wellness.

STRESS RELIEF

When your mind is racing or you feel less than calm, Rock and Roll breathing might help.

5. Sit up straight on the floor or the edge of a chair.

6. Place your hands on your belly.

7. As you inhale, slowly lean forward and expand your belly.

8. As you exhale, squeeze the breath out through your mouth and curl forward while leaning backward; exhale until you're completely empty of breath.

9. Repeat 20 times.

INVIGORATING HA BREATH

Not all breathing is for calming purposes. You can use breathing techniques to empower and to energize yourself as well.

You have probably noticed that martial artists will use breath in this way.

Whenever you feel sluggish or need a pick-me-up, instead of heading to the coffee pot, this technique might help.

Hawaiian Ha Breathing

1. Get comfortably seated.

2. Focus, and hold your attention on your Solar Plexus.

3. Inhale through your nose using your diaphragm.

4. Pause.

5. Exhale slowly through your mouth, twice the duration of your inhale, whilst making a "Haaaaa" sound.

6. Pause.

7. Repeat for as long as you wish to (Surging Life, n.d.).

How do you feel? Invigorated? It's important to frequently take stock of how certain practices affect your body. Keeping a journal near you can help you to build a daily practice based on reflection and the notes you record in the journal. If one thing works, continue it. If you aren't quite feeling it, try something else.

MEDITATION

Meditation is an ancient practice that was once steeped in religion and mysticism. However, as the wellness benefits of meditation have been discovered, the practice has become increasingly popular in secular life as well. In his book *The Relaxation Response,* Dr. Herbert Benson showed how meditation acts as an antidote to stress. His book topped the bestseller lists in the mid-70s and the information is still relevant today.

Meditation is the process of training your mind to focus and redirect your thoughts. It can be used to create and support well-being in numerous ways, including increasing your awareness, developing concentration, creating positive outlooks, increasing pain tolerance, and reducing stress, among other benefits.

You don't need anything specific to start a meditation practice. A few minutes a day is a great way to start. Finding your "sweet spot" is important so that you can more easily create consistency (See Chapter 17, Remember Your ABCs). Remember that intentional breathing (five breaths in and out) can also be a good start as you find your meditational sweet spot.

You'll recognize your sweet spot when your body calms down at the same time that your monkey mind is replaced by a calm, clear mind that just observes thought rather than being "in" the process of thought.

When you're focused on your breathing, this, itself, is a form of meditation.

Numerous meditation styles exist. Perhaps experiment with a few until you find one that you're comfortable with. Free, guided meditations can be found online. If you feel you need more guidance in a group environment, a meditation class can help support your effort and create community at the same time, which, as we'll see, is another important facet of well-being.

Numerous studies have been done on meditation and its benefits. I have listed a few supported by research.

Stress Reduction. – Reducing stress has become one of the main reasons people try meditation. Usually, physical and mental stress can cause increased levels of the stress hormone cortisol. This is also known as the "fight or flight" hormone. In times when there was a real threat, such as imminent danger from a saber-toothed tiger, cortisol could save a caveman's life. Nowadays, our stress can be triggered by things other than the threat of being eaten. The effects of stress can cause disrupted sleep, increase blood pressure, and higher risk of depression and anxiety. Research has shown that meditation can improve symptoms of stress-related conditions such as irritable bowel syndrome, post-traumatic stress disorder, and fibromyalgia (Thorpe, 2017).

Anxiety Control. – Simply put, less stress can lead to less anxiety. An eight-week study of mindfulness meditation helped participants reduce their anxiety and symptoms of anxiety disorders such as phobias, social anxiety, paranoid thoughts, panic attacks, and obsessive-compulsive behaviors (Thorpe, 2017).

Emotional Health Support. – Studies have shown that some forms of meditation can create a more positive outlook on life. In a controlled study, electrical activity was monitored in the brains of those who practiced mindfulness meditation compared with the brains of other who didn't meditate; results showed measurable changes in activity of those who meditated in the areas of the brain related to positive thinking and optimism (Thorpe, 2017).

Enhance Self Awareness. – Self-Inquiry and similar styles of meditation can help you "know yourself," which can provide the essential foundation for taking positive steps in a well-being program.

Lengthens Attention Span. – Several types of meditation may build your ability to redirect and maintain attention.

May Reduce Age-Related Memory Loss. – The improved focus you can gain through regular meditation may increase memory capacity and mental clarity. These benefits can help fight age-related memory loss and dementia.

Can Generate Kindness. – Metta is a type of meditation that's also called loving-kindness meditation. It begins with developing kind thoughts and feelings towards yourself, then moves outward. Metta has been shown to increase positivity, empathy, and compassionate behavior.

Fight Addictions. – Meditation develops mental discipline and willpower and can help you avoid triggers. This can help you recover from addiction, lose weight, and redirect other unwanted habits.

Improves Sleep. – Meditation can help you relax and control the "monkey mind" that can interfere with sleep. This can both shorten the time it takes to fall asleep and improve sleep quality.

Helps Control Pain. – Meditation can diminish the perception of pain in the brain. This can help treat chronic pain when used alongside medical care.

Can Decrease Blood Pressure. – Several studies (Bai et al., 2015; Koike & Cardoso, 2014; Jennings, 2017) have shown that meditation can control blood pressure by relaxing the nerve signals that coordinate heart function, tension in the blood vessels, and the "fight or flight response."

The benefits of meditation are quite compelling. Perhaps give it a try in your own way and see where it leads you on the path to well-being.

CHAPTER 4
CULTURES OF CURES AND HEALING

As early as the 5th century B.C.E., the historian and physician **Herodotus** observed that different natural mineral springs, in various parts of Greece, had a plethora of therapeutic properties. He developed a rudimentary system for differentiating the therapeutic indications of various types of mineral waters. He also recommended that 21-day courses of spa therapy be undertaken at certain times of the year.

Hippocrates, the Father of Medicine, was also the father of hydrotherapy and balneotherapy (bath therapy). He was very much interested in the therapeutic properties of various waters, which he saw were either rain fed, as in lakes or marshes, or from subterranean aquifers, as in mineral springs that come bubbling out of the rocks. He theorized that their differing curative properties came from their differing contents of various minerals, like iron, copper, silver, gold or sulfur. Within the Hippocratic writings is the remarkable classic *Airs, Waters and Places.*

Not only did his writing concern itself with the curative effects of various mineral waters, but also with the therapeutic properties of the airs and microclimates of various locales. Hippocrates' holistic thinking was adopted in the field of balneotherapy in the European spa resorts. Still today, the central attraction of these resorts consists of the mineral waters and their curative properties.

Unlike the "quick fix" therapies of modern society, true balneological cures take time. After all, ailments most likely didn't develop in a day. Allowing your body to heal them will also take more than a day. Following what Hippocrates recommended, almost all the spas I visited offered a healing stay of 21 days. Many of the locals whom I met along the journey were there for that amount of time, swore by the results, and returned multiple times during the year. For them, health and well-being weren't just a priority; they were a lifestyle.

CHAPTER 5
BULGARIA

AN INTRIGUING COUNTRY WITH A RICH HISTORY.

Whenever I mention Bulgaria, I often get quizzical looks. Even a local in the capital city of Sophia asked me, "Why on earth do you come to Bulgaria?" Sometimes, it takes different eyes to see the beauty of a place.

Located on the Black Sea with miles of stunning coastline, Bulgaria is a small country with a rich history.

It is definitely an off-the-beaten-path destination as far as European travel goes. Yet, I found Bulgaria to be a remarkable country with multiple mineral springs, each with its own healing properties. These same waters were used by the Greeks and Romans to heal and rejuvenate (Mays, 2018).

At the time I began searching for natural healing, I had been diagnosed with osteoarthritis in my knees and I had seriously damaged my rotator cuff and bicep from exercise.

I spent months researching locations that I felt would help me to heal my knees, shoulder and bicep in a natural way without meds.

I'm personally very tied to the sea on many levels and actively sought thalassotherapy treatments on my journey. Thalassotherapy comes from the Greek word for 'the sea,' *thalassa,* and 'healing,' *therapeia*. The sea's curative powers were lauded by both Plato and Euripides who respectively said, "The sea cures all ailments of man" and "The sea washes away all men's illnesses." Plato, Hippocrates, and Aristotle recommended hot seawater baths as treatments.

Indeed, marine air has negative ions that helps in healing (Mason, 2017).

I ended up on the Black Sea at a state-of-the-art spa that offered multiple healing modalities and rivaled any place I had been to in the United States.

The water at the spa was mineralized, pushing up from the earth at great depth. An integrative health physician was overseeing expertly trained therapists, and I can honestly say that my experience was nothing short of remarkable. To begin treatments, I was required to go over my health history with the doctor. Although she didn't speak English, her manner was kind and understanding. I had a wonderful multilingual translator, Hristina, who helped me through the health questions. Prescription in hand, I began.

Daily treatments included thalassotherapy and water rehabilitation guided by physical therapists. I quickly became a fan of water exercise, also known as hydrokinetic therapy. The water was gentle on my joints and helped to keep me moving fluidly without the force of gravity. When submerged, the body weighs nearly 90% less. The specific mineral composition and temperature of the thermal waters facilitate gradual recovery of muscle strength and joint mobility. It's also fun and relaxing. I thoroughly enjoyed my treatments and therapy in Bulgaria and look forward to returning.

CHAPTER 6

HUNGARY

EPIC THERMAL LAKE BATHING

Hungary is well-known for its bathing culture which dates back to antiquity. Even before actual baths were built, thermal springs were used for healing.

According to writings of the Middle Ages, Saint Elizabeth used the waters of these thermal springs to heal lazars and lepers (Béni, 2017).

Budapest is probably the best-known location in Hungary, especially with the "bath" crowd.

The springs at the base of Gellert Mountain supplied the lower thermal springs district during ancient times. The famous Gellert Bath was built in the center of this district. I had to see this bath for myself, and it was nothing short of magnificent. It felt like being in a castle of exquisite mosaics and labyrinthian corridors. Although a very trendy place in Budapest, I thoroughly enjoyed the experience.

However, I didn't stop there. I was searching for something that the average tourist wouldn't normally experience. A place where those "in the know" might go for a healing experience. The search led me to the charming spa town of Heviz, located roughly a 2-hour drive from Budapest. The lake in Heviz is the crown jewel and one of the most remarkable lakes I have ever experienced.

Lake Heviz is the largest biologically-active thermal lake in the world, with a more than 200-year medical tradition and documented results. Formed thousands of years ago, archeological findings show that the lake was used by the Romans. Legend has it that Emperor Flavius Theodisius had a miraculous healing at the lake.

The traditional Heviz therapy has shown extensive success in the treatment of musculoskeletal disorders. I had found the right place!

The water pushes out of the earth from a 16-foot layer of peat and renews itself roughly every 72 hours. The renewal of the water and, subsequently, of the healing properties it offers was fascinating.

The most unique thing I noticed about Heviz was that every 15 minutes, they announced the time. I found this to be very unusual and initially had no idea what it was about. Then I learned that bathing in the lake without a doctor's prescription was recommended in increments of no more than 30 minutes. The announcement of the time was to keep track of how long you were in. Not knowing any of this, I was happily paddling around for over two hours at a time. The water was so perfect that I literally didn't want to get out. Fortunately, I didn't experience any side effects.

Also interesting to note, everyone was floating vertically in the lake and *not* swimming. They were using noodles that you would see in a swimming pool to float around while chatting. Imagine 500+ people floating in a lake with pool noodles! It was certainly a unique sight! The artwork in town centered around the "noodle culture" and was most original and often amusing.

I have to say that this charming, mostly pedestrian town with a lively bathing culture and healing lake was much more than I could have hoped for.

CHAPTER 7
ROMANIA

SAPROPELIC MUD

R omania, no doubt, brings to mind Transylvania and the stories of Dracula. Yet Romania offers *so much more* than a fictional story made famous by Hollywood.

The region of Transylvania was breathtaking to behold, full of hills, lakes, and castles. Navigating the hairpin turns of the Transfagarasan Highway was both harrowing and exciting, certainly an adventure unto itself!

The people I met along my journey were warm and inviting, and the experience was remarkable. But I digress; healing is a big part of the culture in Romania as well. And it has been for centuries.

In my research, I discovered something called Sapropelic mud. The largest supplier of this mud is from a lake called Techirghiol, located roughly two miles from the Black Sea.

Local lore says that a blind and lame man and his old donkey wandered into the lake, and after 3 days, they were healed. Research began on the lake in 1750 and documented reports of healing were published (Sanatoriul Balnear, n.d.; Techirghiol, 2011). I was beyond intrigued to learn more.

I checked myself into a spa near the lake which offered over 200 treatments, but the focus of the program was the mud. Indeed, there was nothing glamorous about the dark, and rather rancid-smelling black ooze, but it was, undoubtedly, the main reason patients were there. "Mud Robes" were given out at the front desk and were brown instead of white. Made perfect sense. If you weren't doing a mud treatment that day, then you got a white robe.

A prescription for treatments is required. The resident English-speaking doctor asked me in-depth questions about my health history, took my blood pressure, and prescribed a 7-day protocol of treatments, with mud being the star on the wellness stage. So many treatments were available that my head was spinning. In talking to some of the other patients about their treatments, the mud was used for preventative, curative, and rehabilitative purposes, and it worked. The locals returned year after year, some for over 20 years running, to reap the benefits of this "black gold."

The smell was pungent, yet my skin felt amazing afterward, moisturized and silky.

I also felt a sense of overall well-being. I had a noticeable spring in my step unhindered by the joint issues that had plagued me since the fateful waterski accident.

CHAPTER 8

ITALY

VOLCANIC CLAY AND LA VITA BELLA

Just the name Italy can bring to mind the ideal escape filled with fabulous food and wine.

But it doesn't stop there.

An area in Northern Italy is well known for its healing mud and waters. Sister spa towns, Abano Terme' and Montegrotto Terme' are in the spotlight of what is known as "Euganean Thermalism". The towns are primarily designed for spa tourism, and offer a civilized, very Italian experience.

Numerous studies have been conducted on the unique properties of the volcanic clay, thermal water and microorganisms that combine during a two-month "ripening" process and produce documented anti-inflammatory results. The thermal water originates from Monti Lessini in the Venetian Alps and emerges from the earth at over 85 degrees Celsius (185 degrees Fahrenheit).

A prescription for treatment is needed by the resident doctor, as it was in Romania. The appointment began with a blood pressure check and health history discussion, and then the specific temperature of the mud was prescribed.

Interestingly, I discovered that the mud treatments were covered by insurance in Italy if the patient/client had a prescription from their doctor. That speaks volumes about the country's belief in the efficacy of the treatment.

Truth be told, the treatment itself is less than glamorous, but immensely effective in the end.

There are three essential steps:

Spreading of the warm clay/mud

Sweating

Thermal Bathing

Application

The mud/clay is applied to dry skin at a temperature that ranges between 38 to 42 degrees Celsius or 100.4 to 107.6 degrees Fahrenheit.

I basically was lying on a bed of clay/mud and the technician proceeded to cover me entirely from the chest down in mud. Then, a plastic tarp was folded over me. I'm on the claustrophobic side, and the 20 minutes in this mummy-like treatment took *a lot* of calming breathing to get me through what seemed like an eternity. Gratefully, the technician appeared frequently with a towel and water.

Sweat

The heat from the mud/clay opens the pores where nutrients are drawn into your body through the skin, and toxins are released. Sweating profusely under exceptionally warm mud without being able to move felt immensely non-spa-like, but I wasn't here for "foo-foo" treatments. I was here for healing treatments.

Thermal Bathing

I was released from my cocoon and the technician showered me with thermal water from a hose, which reminded me of washing a horse. Definitely not glamorous!

After that, I submerged into a thermal tub with water at a temperature ranging between 36 and 38 degrees Celsius, 96.8-100.4 degrees Fahrenheit where the sweating continued.

To help reactivate skin circulation, a massage was recommended but optional.

Research has shown that this particular therapy helps to rebalance your bone tissues' remineralization (Centro Studi, n.d.).

Overall, the treatment had a very positive effect on my joints and general feeling of well-being.

When not submerged in the thermal pools or in the mud/clay "mummy" therapy, I spent my time biking in the beautiful rolling hills of Northern Italy. Here, it truly is "la vita bella."

CHAPTER 9

GERMANY

WHERE NATURAL HEALING OPPORTUNITIES ABOUND

Experiencing the saunas, healing waters, and moor mud in Germany was a special treat. Wellness is taken very seriously in Germany, as evidenced by the sheer number of healing locales.

Basing myself in Berlin, I discovered the wealth of springs and spas in nearby towns. A particular favorite was Bad Saarow where the use of saunas and thermal water for healing were mainstays.

The nutrient rich saltwater rises from 13,000 feet beneath the spa. The spa itself was magnificent. Huge, clean, and modern, it seemed out of place in the little spa town.

It had multiple bathing areas and extensive locker facilities.

One bathing area included underwater sound therapy to create what I felt was an unforgettably relaxing experience. Floating in warm mineral water with classical music piping in under the water was magical. And to top it all off, the ceiling had slowly changing colored lights, as did the pool. Water, sound, and light therapy in one place: the experience was all-encompassing. I will be searching for this again in all parts of the world. I felt this combination of therapies transported my soul as well as relaxed my body in a way I had never before experienced.

The saunas were housed in a separate zone from the bathing area and had a culture of their own. Swimsuits were not allowed; however, towels were used by some of the guests. There were unisex showers, and everyone went about freely, without concern. I understand that nudity is an integral part of the German spa culture. Nevertheless, my American sense of spa culture kept me clinging to my towel. The spa attendant explained that to reap the full benefits of the sauna, sweating needed to happen unimpeded by cloth of any kind. I kindly thanked her for the information, and entered the sauna still wrapped in my towel.

One particular treat was a daily baking of bread **inside** one of the saunas, which had a built-in oven. It was an event that I had never experienced anywhere else! The smell of baking bread evokes an almost universal sense of comfort. And inside a sauna with a spectacular view of the lake made it all the more special.

In speaking with several guests at this German sauna, they told me that their doctors told them to go to the sauna as many days as possible because it reduces the chance of heart attacks. In doing some research, I found a study (Masakazu et al., 2001) that proved this to be true. Also, their visits were covered by German insurance as preventive medicine. Great benefit indeed.

We can hope that one day healing and preventative treatments will be covered by insurance in many more countries around the world.

Additional benefits of sauna treatment can include:

1. Improves cardiovascular performance.

2. Aids in recovery after intense physical activity.

3. Flushes out toxins through sweating.

4. Relieves stress.

5. Induces deeper sleep.

6. Helps fight illness.

7. Cleanses the skin.

8. Burns more calories.

9. Provides a haven for rest or socialization (Finnleo, n.d.).

10. Reduces the incidence of Alzheimer's in men (Laukkanen, Kunutsor, Kauhanen, & Laukkanen, 2017).

The sauna in Germany was a traditional Finnish sauna whereby heat is used to warm the air. I felt that I needed more time in research than I had available in Germany. So, I decided to go to a local sauna, which happened to be an infrared sauna. These types of saunas use light to create heat (Bauer, 2017). Knowing the stated benefits of a sauna, I went four times per week for one month, and usually after a workout. I noticed I was less sore after workouts, generally more relaxed, and was sleeping better.

Also, because an infrared sauna uses light to heat your body instead of heat, I found it much more comfortable to stay in longer, allowing me to get all the benefits of sweating.

The place I found had a one-person sauna, so, the towel issue didn't come into play like it did in Germany. I did miss the comforting smell of baking bread however!

CHAPTER 10

AT THE CENTER
EARTHING / GROUNDING

EARTHING DEFINITION

Through the travels and experiences I've shared so far, you can see that the healing elements don't include modern or high-tech equipment. Rather, all is provided by the gifts of Mother Nature and the earth we inhabit.

Quite literally, the ground beneath your feet is a wellspring of healing. Think about how you feel when walking barefoot along the shore or on dew-laden grass. Or playing in the ocean or swimming in a lake. These are all part of life's simple pleasures which fill us with a sense of calm, of well-being. Perhaps you even feel a sense of warmth or tingling, adding an extra spark to the moment. Well, there might just be a scientific reason behind that.

Current research explains this as bioelectricity. It's a powerful yet invisible force experienced in our daily lives. We are bioelectrical beings with bodily activities such as the heart and nervous systems functioning electrically. And the earth is an electrical planet. Through direct contact with the surface of the Earth, whether barefoot in the grass or playful submersion in its waters, the very action provides us with an infusion of earth's energy (Ober, 2014).

The earth provides negatively-charged ions that can help reduce and neutralize the free radicals in the body that cause disease and cellular destruction.

One of the major benefits of Earthing is that it appears to assuage inflammation through the transfer of negatively-charged electrons from the surface of the Earth into the body (where the electrons neutralize positively-charged, destructive free radicals involved in chronic inflammation) (Chevalier, Sinatra, Oschman, Sokal, & Sokal, 2012).

According to Ober (2014), Earth's energy can "restore and stabilize" the bioelectrical circuitry that:

1. governs your physiology and organs,

2. harmonize your basic biological rhythms,

3. boost self-healing mechanisms,

4. reduce inflammation and pain, and

5. improve your sleep and feeling of calmness.

All this from just connecting to the earth in some way.

The research in this book suggests that all of us are living on a global treatment table. What a gift! Now all we need to do is to access it.

Maybe a far-flung beach vacation isn't possible right now, but it makes sense to embrace nature and to incorporate Earthing into our daily lives in some way. Let's discuss how we end up disconnected and how we can reconnect.

Today's modern lifestyle is far from that of our ancestors. Going barefoot has been replaced with strapping on insulating rubber or plastic-soled shoes. Sleeping on the ground isn't typically part of our day as it was in more ancient times. Think back to times you've spent a weekend at the ocean or lake, or even a barefoot picnic in the park; remember how fabulous you feel after.

Our connection to the earth can manifest significant benefits to our overall well-being.

Many people I've spoken with during my journey told me that they specifically moved to a location of sun, sand, sea, and/or plentiful nature for health reasons. They didn't know the science behind Earthing, but they did know that their health improved and so did their outlook. Coincidence?

Scientific research has shown Earthing benefits in assuaging inflammation (the mothership of chronic disease), cardiovascular disease, blood thickness, inflammation, nervous system imbalances, and diabetes (James Oschman, n.d.).

Biophysicist James Oschman (2000), sums up Earthing this way:

"The moment your foot touches the Earth, or you connect to the Earth through a wire, your physiology changes. An immediate normalization begins. And an anti-inflammatory switch is turned on. People stay inflamed because they never connect with the Earth, the source of free electrons which can neutralize the free radicals in the body that cause disease and cellular destruction. Earthing is the easiest and most profound lifestyle change anyone can make."

Now that you have some information on why to incorporate Earthing into your daily life, let's look at ways to give it a try! Earthing is a simple, natural, low-cost, effective, and doable activity that has the potential to promote health and healing in the body.

A barefoot stroll or long salt bath can help raise your spirits as well, which is a fabulous benefit any way you look at it.

Walking/ Standing

Take off your shoes and walk around your backyard or at a park for 40 minutes Even standing on concrete (preferable wet) can do the trick. It's important to know that you need a conductive surface so that your body can draw from the Earth's electrons.

I mentioned a few surfaces that serve to do this. Note that wood, asphalt, and vinyl aren't conductive services.

Bathing

Adding Himalayan salt to your bath can add valuable minerals to the water for absorption through your skin. This is the closest thing I've found to creating the environment of the healing springs I encountered in my travels. I like to add about five pounds per bathtub. I recommend that you experiment to see where you feel a soothing benefit without skin irritation. I was told at the various spas that three times per week for 4 weeks is optimal for an anti-inflammatory result

Sleeping/Working

Most likely, sleeping on the bare ground isn't a consistent option for most. Here's where a little modern technology comes in.

You can sleep on a conductive bed mat or sit and work with your feet on a conductive floor mat connected to the Earth via a wire to a properly grounded electrical outlet inside a home or office (or to a grounding rod outside). These systems incorporate carbon or silver mesh to conduct the Earth's energy and can be used in bed, while watching TV or reading, or while working at a desk (Earthing, n.d.).

With several options readily available, you can conduct your own test on how Earthing can have a positive effect on your well-being, starting today.

If not Now, When?

CHAPTER 11

SRI LANKA

AYURVEDA AS TRUE MEDICINE

What Is Ayurvedic Medicine?

Ayurvedic medicine ("Ayurveda" for short) is one of the world's oldest holistic ("whole-body") healing systems. It was developed more than 3,000 years ago in India.

Ayurvedic treatment combines products mainly derived from plants, (but at times including animal, metal, and mineral ingredients), with diet, exercise, and lifestyle.

According to ancient Sri Lankan writings, Ayurveda was practiced by kings starting as early as the 4th century BCE. It's based on the belief that health and wellness depend on a delicate balance between the mind, body, and spirit. The main goal of Ayurveda is to promote good health, not to fight disease. I spoke with patients who were undergoing treatments designed for specific medical issues, and they swore that Ayurveda saved their lives. More on this later.

In the United States, it's considered a form of complementary and alternative medicine (CAM) with no formal regulation.

However, In Sri Lanka, Ayurveda **IS** medicine, and there are around 16,800 registered Ayurvedic medical officers. More than 5,000 of these are academically and institutionally qualified doctors.

Ayurveda and Life Energy

Ayurveda seeks to restore balance in every area of your body, mind, and spirit.

When something disrupts this balance, you get sick. Among the factors that can upset this balance are genes, injuries, climate and seasonal change, age, stress, and emotions.

Those who practice Ayurveda believe every person is made of five basic elements found in the universe: space, air, fire, water, and earth.

These combine in the human body to form three life forces or energies, called doshas. They control how your body works. They are Vata dosha (space and air); Pitta dosha (fire and water); and Kapha dosha (water and earth).

The belief is that we all inherit a unique mix of the three doshas. But one is usually stronger than the others. Each one controls a different body function. It's believed that your chances of getting sick, and any health issues you may develop, are linked to the balance of your doshas.

Vata Dosha

This dosha controls very basic body functions such as cell division. It also controls your breathing, mind, heart function, blood flow, and ability to get rid of waste through your intestines. Things that can disrupt it include eating again too soon after a meal, grief, fear, and staying up too late.

Pitta Dosha

This dosha controls your metabolism, digestion, and certain hormones that are linked to your appetite.

Things that can disrupt it are eating sour or spicy foods and spending too much time in the sun.

Kapha Dosha

This life force controls weight, muscle growth, body strength and stability, and your immune system.

You can disrupt it by sleeping during the day, eating too many sweet foods, and consuming anything that contains too much salt or water.

Ayurvedic Treatment

An Ayurvedic practitioner will create a treatment plan specifically designed for you, considering your unique physical and emotional makeup, your primary life force (dosha), and the balance between all three of these elements.

A cleansing process called *Panchakarma* is designed to restore harmony and balance, while subsequently reducing symptoms.

The Ayurvedic practitioner might use methods of blood purification, massage with medical oils, herbs, and enemas or laxatives.

I can say without hesitation that my Panchakarma was incredibly effective, and that I was surprised by both the process and the results.

Remember that it's always best to talk to your doctor before you try Ayurveda or any other alternative or complementary medical treatment, especially if you're currently on a treatment program.

My Experience in Sri Lanka.

After joining some dear friends in the north of Sri Lanka, I found myself interested in exploring more of this fascinating country and learning more about the history and culture.

I hired an energetic English-speaking driver and set out on a southernly route on a two-lane winding road with harrowing passing practices not for the faint of heart.

About three hours into the journey, we stopped at an expansive herb garden installment. I exited the car for a stretch and was offered a tour of the impressively organized garden of healing plants.

At the end of the tour, I sat down to have tea with the senior herbalist and owner of the garden. He shared that his family were herbalists to the kings for over 1,900 years. Every generation before had been taught the secrets of herbal healing, which is one of the foundations of Ayurveda practice.

Then I learned something about health and well-being that I had never heard before. A distinction exists between the physical body and the body of internal organs. These organs form an important integrated system which supports overall wellness and should be considered as a whole, not as independent organs such as kidney, liver, stomach, spleen, pancreas, etc.

This system both produces and stores energy, working basically as a "second brain" regarding functions of wellness.

For this internal organ system to operate at an optimal level, any blockages should be removed. So many questions came to mind, but the most pressing was, of course: "How can blockages be removed?" The herbalist looked at me quizzically and said, "Like our kings did…with a Panchakarma."

He went on to explain that it is a cleansing performed by an Ayurvedic doctor based on my specific needs. I told him I felt fine, and what he said next hit me like a rock. "Maybe you do, but your organs might not be fine, and that *will* catch up to your physical body." I was now more intrigued than ever, so I asked his recommendation for an Ayurvedic doctor. He told me to continue south to a little clinic on the southern shore of the island. He didn't have an address, but he said that all the locals know the place. Ask around and I'll find it. Okay…

Also, he specifically told me not to go to a practice inside a tourist hotel because it wasn't authentic. He obviously knew that I wouldn't be able to tell authentic Ayurveda from "tourist" Ayurveda, and I was going to take his advice.

After another long and winding three-hour journey complete with multiple pauses to ask locals about this mysterious clinic, I ended up at the end of a dirt road about one mile from a popular beach area called Mirissa.

I was greeted by the loud squawks of peacocks flying (yes, flying!) from palm tree to palm tree. What an amazing sight and a wonderful welcome.

Doctor Seth, a man in his 30s, greeted me. His wife (also a doctor) had created a lovely boutique clinic nestled in a palm forest. With only seven working rooms at the time, I was fortunate to be a guest, especially so last-minute.

Dr. Seth , whose full name is Sethsiri Wijaysinghe, is a generational Ayurvedic doctor. He is a detox specialist who also works in his family's Ayurvedic hospital in Colombo, with capacity to treat over 400 patients. I was inspired to hear that a large hospital was devoted to just Ayurvedic treatments.

My interest piqued about this ancient healing technique, I was eager to get started. After settling into my room and a delicious vegetarian lunch, I met with Dr, Seth for a consultation. Unlike other doctors I had seen, he didn't ask any health history questions. Instead, he started with a "reading" of my pulse for over 15 minutes, elevating one of four fingers at a time. I had never experienced a pulse reading like this, and it was fascinating.

His reading was nothing short of mystical. He began to tell me in great detail about a past ailment I had *over 20 years ago.* It was the very thing that hospitalized me twice. His evaluation was very specific and detailed, and I was staring at him in disbelief. How could he tell that from my pulse?

He then began to talk to me about a fairly recent negative situation in my life and how it was affecting both my mental and emotional well-being. He didn't specify the situation; however, he did tell me that it was weighing heavily on my heart and on my spirit. I couldn't believe the accuracy of his evaluations in both cases, and now I was admittedly freaked out. No doctor I had seen prior, in any country in the world, had told me without any prior knowledge of my situation about past ailments and recent events affecting my well-being. Especially by solely reading my pulse! I mean, this was a huge WOW moment in my journey. After I calmed down from the shock, he told me not to worry, and that everything was treatable. He suggested a modified Panchakarma. Panchakarma means "five cleansings" and involves some rather unusual treatments designed to unblock the system. I had no idea what was coming next, but I was so astounded by the accuracy of his diagnosis that l was just going to run with it.

Doctor Seth felt that I didn't need the full treatment plan, so he modified my program. I stayed for eight days and underwent what I consider one of the most transformative programs of body, mind, and spirit that I've ever experienced.

Each treatment has a name, as does the process. In a nutshell, Purvakarma prepares your body for a cleanse, Panchkarma removes the toxins through natural means of elimination, and Paschatkarma supports the rejuvenation process.

Each day I had massages with specially selected oils, which, by the way, were the most pleasant of the treatments. The others...not so much.

My body was prepared with specific foods for three days. The massage and the specific diet were parts of the Purvakarma stage.

Then, I began an extremely intense intestinal cleansing called Virechana, which started with taking three little herbal pills at a specific time given to me by the doctor. All I can say is that it's a good thing that I didn't know what to expect beforehand because I'm not certain I would have gone through with it. The only way I can describe it is intentionally-induced food poisoning for six hours!

The next day, I rested from that cleanse. I was weak, and, honestly, quite traumatized, but I was committed. After that experience, how bad could the rest of it be?

My next treatment was called Nasya, designed to clear out my nasal passages. This treatment, for me, was *exceptionally* unpleasant. Yet, the results were very real. After years of a pesky post-nasal drip, I felt completely clear.

The next day I had a treatment called Netra Basti which involved pouring warm ghee in my eyes. Ghee is basically butter without the milk solids. Having my vision blurred by warm butter while I rolled my eyes around in it was beyond foreign to me, and most unpleasant. But, I was trusting the process, and was determined to do whatever was prescribed by the doctor.

The food I was given after the Virechana was very light so that the renewal process was supported.

That said, at the end of my eight-day treatment program, I felt immensely renewed – as if an enormous emotional weight had been lifted from my heart. My spirit was light and free again, and my body felt terrific.

When I think back on my treatments, I had no idea what a positive effect they would have on my emotional well-being. My experience with Ayurveda was a definite first for me on so many levels. To this day, I'm still processing my experience, and remain very grateful. Would I do it again? Resoundingly, yes.

During my stay, I had the opportunity to talk with the other patients at the clinic. What I discovered floored me. Three out of the four clients were fourth-stage cancer patients who were given a "death sentence" by their doctors in their home countries. Although they were told that they had only months to live, they came every year to see Dr. Seth, and had done so *for years*. I learned of their battles with cancer and how the treatments have literally saved their lives and given them back a quality of life that they never thought possible. One patient, who was diagnosed with an "incurable liver disease," by his Western doctors was cured by Dr. Seth.

A large inspiration for this book was my experience in Sri Lanka with Ayurveda and how it ended up helping a dear friend back in the States.

Ayurveda in the U.S.

My friend Roy had suffered for decades from a dry cough that tormented him daily and was excruciating to hear. He used an inhaler multiple times per day and I was very concerned about the long-term effects of this. I was also concerned about the long-term effects on his neck from the frequent coughing, which involved a whiplash type movement.

In remembering my treatment in Sri Lanka, I asked Roy if he would be willing to try Ayurveda for his cough. He was very open to it, which launched me into a search for a practitioner in his area who most resonated with what I had experienced in Sri Lanka. After over 20 calls and multiple conversations, I found a doctor with whom I felt confident. We discussed Roy's condition, and an appointment was set. What happened next was nothing short of miraculous.

After only one treatment, his decades-long violent coughing was quelled. Roy implemented a diet change along with herbal treatments and a daily Nasya. His use of the inhaler has dropped significantly as well.

In my experience, Ayurveda had remarkable healing effects for both Roy and for myself.

If you feel that Ayurveda might be something to look into, here are a few tips.

As I had mentioned earlier, no standardization of Ayurvedic practice exists in the U.S., so finding an experienced Ayurvedic doctor with requisite training requires a substantial amount of patience and willingness to follow your intuition. In calls, ask where they studied, and how long they have been practicing. One especially helpful tip is to speak directly with the doctor yourself.

When a doctor answered the phone him or herself or called me back directly to discuss my concerns and/or condition, I had a direct connection and was able to follow my intuition more clearly.

Ultimately, I can honestly tell you that what I experienced in my own healing, the miraculous stories I heard from other patients at the clinic in Sri Lanka, and what I witnessed with Roy are all very real.

These are the possible benefits that Dr. Seth told me about a Panchakarma, and which I confirmed with the other guests at the clinic:

- Eliminates toxins from the body.

- Balances the doshas.

- Reduces stress and relaxes the body.

- Slows aging process and increases the lifespan.

- Increases glow and luster of skin.

- Boosts body immunity and body energy level.

- Enhances strength, energy, vitality, and mental clarity.

- Reduces dependence on alcohol, tobacco, and drugs.

- Helps to implement healthy diet and lifestyle.

Remember to always check with your current doctor if you're currently under any type of medical treatment or supervision before beginning any type of complementary or alternative program.

CHAPTER 12
THAILAND

WELLNESS IS A WAY OF LIFE.

Also known as "The Land of Smiles," Thailand was a most enjoyable stop on my journey to find and experience wellness solutions, and one that always calls me to return.

In my many years of receiving different massage treatments, I truly felt a new sense of rejuvenation on multiple levels, after experiencing traditional Thai massage.

I experienced a kind of relaxation that was beyond just physical, which was a first for me.

I can describe the physical treatment itself as being akin to a relaxing session of Yoga – yet without me having to actually do anything. Beyond that, there was a very real element of spirituality in the treatment I experienced. My therapist prayed before beginning the massage which was the first time I had experienced something like that.

I learned that the core objective of a traditional Thai massage is to provide enhanced physical, psychological, and spiritual healing, and a minimum period of 1.5 hours is recommended. Because I wished to fully experience this very cultural treatment, I went with it.

I began my massage by changing into what looked like loose pajamas to wear during the treatment, which allowed full range of motion during the massage process. I was on a padded mat on the floor, which was quite different from the traditional massage tables I've experienced.

Being on the floor gives the therapist a greater level of freedom of movement to use body weight and his/her feet (yes, feet) during the massage.

Oils or lotions are not used during a traditional Thai massage. Friction is actually an integral part of the massage process.

Thai massage is considered a therapeutic form of health restoration via the increase of blood-flow, rehabilitation of dysfunctional or weak organs, promotion of correct posture, and the attainment of optimal relaxation.

The foundation of Thai therapeutic massage has its core principles embedded within the concept of anatomy energy lines, also known as

"Sen Lines." The human anatomy is believed to consist of a total of 72,000 Sen lines upon which Chinese acupuncture also heavily relies.

For me, Thai massage in particular was such an overwhelmingly effective experience that I continue it even now.

In my experience, I believe that finding a Thai massage therapist with education or a background in Thailand is very helpful for the overall experience and results. It ensures they have a special connection to this ancient cultural tradition that cannot be taught simply by technique alone.

When calling to find a Thai massage therapist, ask for training and experience details. Don't be afraid to also ask for references, especially if they are practicing outside of a clinic or commercial massage location. If your area offers a Thai massage as part of a larger menu of massages, definitely ask about training and experience.

To further assist you, the American Massage Therapy Association provides a database of certified massage therapists on their website.

Sound Therapy

Sound healing therapy uses aspects of music or combined notes to improve your physical and emotional health and well-being. You know how singing along to your favorite tune lifts your spirit? Or maybe dancing (like nobody is watching) to a drumbeat or music gives you a sense of joy? This is part of sound therapy!

Healing with sound has been traced back to ancient Greece when Pythagoras used music to cure mental disorders. Throughout human history, music has been used to boost morale in military troops, (the USO), help people work faster and more productively, and even ward off evil spirits by chanting.

Science has revealed that the human body is basically a vibrational frequency entity. Each cell in your body emits and receives frequencies of sound. You can think of a sick, or damaged, cell as an out-of-tune instrument.

Sound therapy can identify these out-of-tune frequencies. When therapeutic sounds, or frequencies, are introduced into your body, your brain can then send these in-tune or corrected frequencies to the damaged cells.

The result is a healing, or "tuning-up" process that can reduce stress levels and boost immune functions.

Elements of sound therapy include:

- listening to music

- singing along to music

- moving to the beat of the music

- meditating

- playing an instrument

I experienced a wonderful sound therapy session in Thailand using singing bowls. A historical healing method, singing bowl therapy dates back to the 12th century and has been used for meditation and rituals in Tibetan culture. Bowls produce a deep, penetrating sound that's used to relax and repair the mind. Goldsby et al. (2016) found that singing bowl meditation can reduce stress, anger, depression, and fatigue.

My particular treatment in Thailand was designed to balance my chakra system. At the time, I didn't even know that chakra systems could be unbalanced!

The therapist told me that each chakra is associated with a certain key. She then proceeded to play several bowls, each in the corresponding key, for roughly 10 minutes near each chakra. The sound resonated in a vibration I could actually feel in my body. It was otherworldly. At one point, I felt like I was floating weightless in the sound bath, devoid of mental, emotional, or physical restrictions, pain, chatter, or sense of time and space.

After the treatment, I felt an overwhelming sense of peace, well-being, and centeredness.

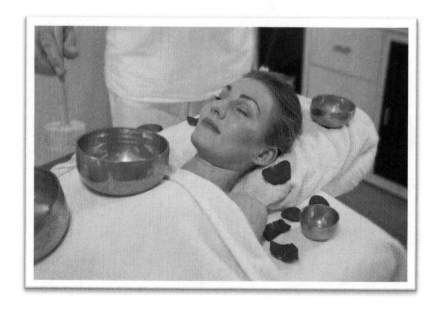

Listening to music has no big risk, and the benefits can be extensive. Experimenting with sounds that work for you can also be fun! So, what are some options to try right now?

Many different types of sound therapy are available, including vibrational sound therapy, which uses special sounds that produce vibrations thought to improve brain waves. Not all have been proven, but with such little risk and such great potential reward, why not give one a try?

Finding a live singing bowl therapy session may not be the most convenient, so I have several singing bowl downloads on my phone that I use during meditation or while stretching.

Another type of sound therapy I use frequently is brainwave entrainment. This is also known as Binaural Beats and can easily be downloaded to your computer or phone. The specific sound stimulates the brain into a specific state to encourage your brain waves to align to the frequency of the beat. Depending on what I'm trying to accomplish, I select a track that helps me to focus, change my state, relax, or induce sleep.

Vibroacoustic therapy

Have you ever been a passenger in a car and lulled to sleep by the consistent vibration of the engine? It can be exceptionally calming.

Vibration is believed to affect your body's functions, such as blood pressure and breathing. Vibroacoustic therapy uses audible sound vibrations to improve health and lower stress. This type of sound therapy involves speakers imbedded in recliners, mattresses, and special mats to transmit music.

Chanting

Chanting or repeating mantras or prayers is an easy and accessible way to put sound therapy into your life today. Chanting an affirmation can create a positive vibration. You can create your own affirmation which aligns with your intentions and say or sing it. Get creative and see where it takes you. I often chant in the shower. It adds an interesting dimension to "singing in the shower."

Neurologic music therapy

As we know from experience, music can reduce stress and promote relaxation. It's been shown to be more effective than prescribed medicine in reducing anxiety levels before surgery. According to Quach and Lee (2017), a 30-minute music therapy session combined with traditional care after spinal surgery reduced pain. The therapy is administered by a credentialed provider who assesses the individual's needs. Treatment involves creating, listening, singing, or moving to music. It's used for physical rehabilitation and pain management.

Bonny method

Named after Hellen L. Bonny PhD, the Bonny method integrates guided imagery and classical music to help explore personal growth, consciousness, and transformation. McKinney and Honig (2017) revealed evidence that a series of sessions could improve psychological and physiological health in adults with medical and mental health needs.

Tuning fork therapy

Tuning fork therapy uses calibrated metal tuning forks to apply specific vibrations to different parts of the body.

This can help release tension and energy and promote emotional balance. It is said to work similarly to acupuncture. Needles are replaced by sound frequencies for point stimulation. Research by Masala and Merolle (2017) suggests tuning fork therapy may help relieve muscle and bone pain.

CHAPTER 13

CHINA

THE SEAT OF TCM

Being half Chinese, I grew up with frequent trips to Chinatown to buy medicinal herbs. The pungent smell of boiling elixirs filled our kitchen and seeped into all living spaces in our home.

Recipes for healing everything from headaches to diabetes were passed down through the generations with few changes. Tradition was followed because results were real and had an indeterminable number of human trials to back them up. Nevertheless, I found the odiferous brews offensive.

I asked my mom why we couldn't just use something else that didn't smell so bad. She gave me a stern look and said, "Because Chinese medicine has worked for thousands of years and is natural. Stop asking questions." My mother didn't seem to appreciate my "American curiosity" questioning the ancient healing methods used by her family for millennia.

Although my mother went to Duke Medical School, she always believed in natural medicine. She told me, "Our beliefs can shift the outcome."

Later, her belief would be tested.

In 2000, she was diagnosed with kidney cancer. Every doctor told her to remove the kidney before the condition worsened. If she didn't, the prognosis would be dire. I was beside myself and urged her to follow the doctors' advice and have the surgery. She stood firm that it was her body and, therefore, ultimately, her decision. I couldn't argue with that reasoning. She explained that she believed that her body could heal naturally. Her daily schedule included both acupuncture and acupressure at home. She also traveled to Mexico for an alternative treatment. She turned 92 in 2019 and is cancer-free. I personally witnessed the healing ability of ancient wisdom.

I suppose the use of TCM (Traditional Chinese Medicine) for healing is in my DNA. Indeed, when I blew out my knee in a waterski accident, I chose to have consistent acupuncture and it worked miraculously for pain. Going into it, I sincerely believed it would help, and that was half the battle. I remembered my mom's words: "Belief can shift the outcome." No doubt that's true on both sides of the equation. The lesson: be mindful of what you believe. If you believe you have an incurable disease, you will soon be consumed by it.

Acupuncture is a 3,000-year-old healing technique. It took some time for it to move to the West, however. In 1997, the U.S. National Institutes of Health evaluated and publicized the efficacy and safety of acupuncture. Treatments spanned a wide range of conditions. Today, acupuncture is covered by many insurance plans and is broadly used.

Acupuncture is based on energy flow and balance. In TCM, there are two forces, Yin and Yang. When the body is healthy, Yin and Yang are in balance. Life energy called "Qi" (pronounced *chee*) flows along internal highways called meridians. When the flow is uninterrupted, we're healthy.

However, if the flow is blocked within the body, the balance is disrupted, which can lead to lack of healthy functions, to illness, or to pain.

Acupuncture can release the blocked qi and renew function, allowing for the body's natural healing response to take effect.

Research shows that acupuncture can help ease pain, improve sleep and digestive functions, and help to create a sense of wellbeing ("Health benefits," n.d.).

How Does It Work?

To help the flow of Qi and natural healing, specific anatomic areas known as acupuncture points or acupoints are stimulated. The method most commonly used is inserting fine, sterile needles into the skin.

My most memorable acupuncture experience occurred in Beijing. Although I had had numerous acupuncture treatments in the United States, I wished to experience the treatment in my country of origin. Perhaps my DNA was pulling me back to my roots, perhaps it was simple curiosity, but whatever the reason I was going to do this.

Although I speak several languages, Chinese isn't one of them. In China, not speaking the language made finding a doctor an adventure in itself. After struggling with directions to a clinic given by a local herbalist, a Good Samaritan who was watching my futile attempts to find the clinic led me up a dark, narrow staircase above a bustling restaurant.

I was greeted at the door by the doctor, a small wiry woman with a big smile. I bowed in greeting and she motioned to a treatment table nearby. I sat on the table and pointed to my left knee while making a wincing face. I have found that charades often help when you don't speak the language – not to mention that locals find it immensely amusing.

The doctor motioned to a robe and then to the table. Got it. She removed needles from a sealed plastic bag, motioned for me to lie down and swiftly began to insert them into my knee with quick and skillful taps. I felt a slight pinch but no lasting pain. In prior treatments, I definitely felt more discomfort. Needles were tapped into my ear, shoulders, ankles, and feet as well. Meridian lines are part of a complex system that far exceeded my limited understanding at the time. Since meridians run all along the body, my understanding now is that the other needles were inserted along the same meridians, related ones, or those interconnected with my knee.

The doctor was skillful and precise, so with trust and curiosity, I went with it.

At the end of the treatment, I felt a sense of calm and reduced knee pain. I returned seven times during my stay in Beijing and I became a believer. The pain in my knee was barely discernable, and I wasn't limping anymore. I developed a true reverence for acupuncture and the doctors who practice this ancient form of healing.

Before leaving my final session, I asked how I could keep the treatments going back at home, and the doctor gave me a brochure in Chinese, which I had translated. The translation basically said that the acupoints could be stimulated using pressure, also known as acupressure. I was happy to have found that this can be done at home, and I find it very effective for relieving multiple maladies to this day.

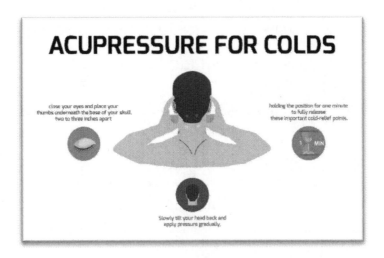

How You Can Use Acupressure at Home

Understanding the complex system of meridians and energy flow can be daunting.

I personally use a few simple acupressure points and leave the more complex treatments to the professionals.

The benefit of acupressure is that it's a very portable treatment; you can do it most anywhere, and even through clothing.

These are some of my "Go-To" treatments:

- **Headache** – Place your finger tip in the center of your forehead directly between the brows. Use a light tapping motion for 15 seconds, stop for 30 seconds, then repeat. Repeat for a few minutes. Move your finger tip across to one inch out from the outer edge of the eyebrow, towards the ear. Use circular pressure on both sides. Do short periods then have a rest in between.

- **Ear ache** – With the palm facing down, pinch up the skin between the 4th and 5th fingers, right in the web. As before, do it for 15 seconds, rest for a short time then repeat.

- **Colds** – Find a spot on the hairline at the back of the skull, about 3 inches either side of the midline. Close your eyes. Put your thumbs on each spot. Slowly tip your head backward while continuing pressure with your thumbs. Hold for 1 minute.

- **Pain** – With palm facing down, spread thumb and forefinger. With the other hand, thumb above and index finger below the web, rub the muscle area between the base of thumb and forefinger for one minute. Switch hands and repeat.

Acupressure can be profoundly relaxing as well as being an effective treatment for a wide variety of conditions. Try a professional treatment to get an idea of just how pleasant and effective it can be.

Reflexology

Reflexology is one of my favorite treatments, and it can be done at home.

Remember the energy channels? They flow to the feet. TCM has detailed foot charts that show how every part of the foot corresponds to an area of the body.

When I'm working, I'll often roll a golf ball under my feet, which stimulates the reflexology points on the bottom of my feet.

Another method I tried were insoles with magnets and contours that continually stimulate my feet. It took a while to get used to, but it eventually became quite soothing.

The important part of trying something new is to listen to your body and follow your own intuitive advice.

To find a qualified professional in TCM, check the National Certification Commission for Acupuncture and Oriental Medicine. Their website provides a database of licensed practitioners.

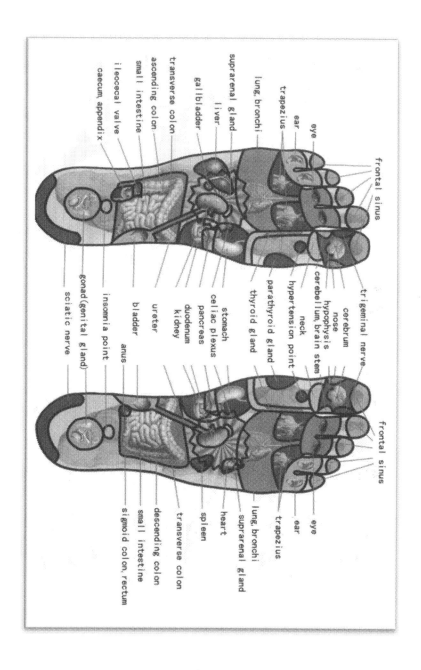

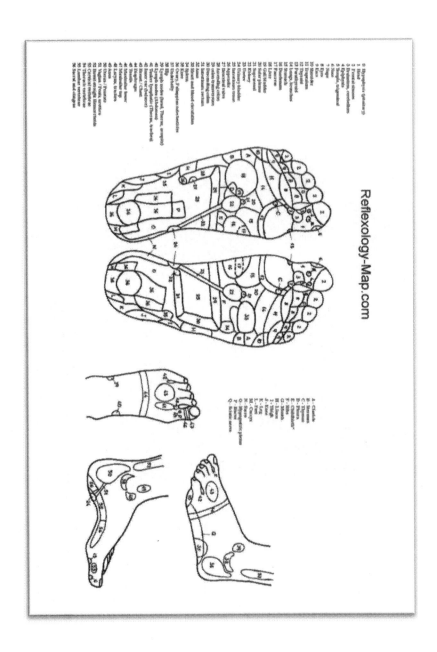

CHAPTER 14
USA

LEADER IN SLEEP MEDICINE

The need for sleep is shared by all creatures and has been since the dawn of time. Rest and the resulting rejuvenation for our body, mind and spirit is a foundation of well-being.

Surprisingly, many people overlook the importance of sleep in a comprehensive wellness program. I myself used to say, "I can sleep when I'm dead." We know how that ended up for me.

I just figured that all was (fairly) well, since I wasn't feeling seriously sleepy or dragging throughout my day.

However, after my continued wellness journey and research, I came to understand that sleep is the (vastly) underrated support system of overall wellness. And what you don't know, *can* hurt you.

Sleep study pioneer William C. Dement, MD, PhD gives an in-depth exploration of sleep in his book *The Promise of SLEEP.* The more we know, the better we can use this information in our daily journey towards improved well-being.

What does sleep do? During sleep, your body restores and repairs itself through creating new cells and removing toxins. If you're consistently not sleeping well, your body's renewing capacity is interrupted, which can result in a lack of energy, decreased feelings of well-being, and faster effects of aging.

According to National Geographic's August 2018 special edition on sleep, sleeping less than six hours a night regularly creates a higher risk of depression, psychosis, stroke and obesity. Bottom line is that sleeplessness disrupts your well-being (Finkel, 2018).

If you're one of the many who struggle to get a good night's sleep, you need to learn how to combat sleep disorders.

There could be several reasons why you might not be sleeping as well as possible.

There are two very clear parts of the sleep equation. The first is *falling* asleep and the second is *staying* asleep. Some people can easily fall asleep; however, their sleep is interrupted throughout the night.

There are understandable temporary reasons why your sleep could be interrupted, such as taking care of young children or older or ailing loved ones.

However, other, less temporary, factors can lead to a lack of sleep as well. These include bad sleep habits, medications, continuing stress, anxiety, and getting older.

Research in sleep and aging done by Sonia Ancoli-Israel, PhD the Center of Circadian Biology at UC San Diego has shown that although sleep interruption and lower sleep requirements have been labeled as simply "part of the aging process," there's a definite distinction (Neikrug & Ancoli-Israel, 2009).

Regarding interrupted sleep as we age, she states that "it's not aging per se that results in poor sleep, but rather the things that go along with aging."

And what are those things? Per the research, poor sleep in older adults is most often tied to medical issues, medications, and changes in circadian rhythm.

Regarding the idea that older adults require less sleep, Dr Anocli-Israel's research has shown that the actual *need* for sleep does not change; however, the *ability* to sleep does change with age (Neikrug & Ancoli-Israel, 2009).

In women, hormonal fluctuations when pregnant or in the process of menopause can also affect restful sleep.

Because sleep is so essential for our well-being, understanding the elements that comprise and elicit "good sleep" is important. Let's look at six components that make up the "good sleep" equation.

Duration. To begin with, there's more to true quality sleep than how long you sleep.

Duration is very important, and there's little you can do to "catch up" after you've had a very short night's sleep. Targeting between seven and nine hours is a good rule of thumb.

Sleep depth

This is the part of your night that you spend in restorative phases, namely deep sleep and REM sleep. These are the phases where you recover and rejuvenate most from physical and emotional strain. I have found that releasing worries and concerns through a bedtime ritual or journaling can help to quell the nagging voices that keep you from fully restorative sleep.

Interruptions

The number and length of your significant sleep interruptions can reset your sleep cycles. Try setting your alarm a little later if necessary. If you continuously feel tired upon waking up, it could be from unknown interruptions, which I talked about earlier in this chapter.

Bed- and rise-time regularity

There's growing evidence that regularity of bedtime and rise time has many impacts on your quality of sleep. Following a regular routine will help your body automatically prepare for sleep, and you'll fall asleep easier.

Medical Reasons for Sleep Problems

Many people, at all ages, have medical conditions that keep them from sleeping well. Such conditions include insomnia, enlarged prostate (causing frequent urination), nightmares, restless leg syndrome (jerking while asleep), sleep apnea (a feeling of choking that wakes you up), and/or snoring.

If you're finding that lack of sleep is impacting the functionality or quality of your life, it might be time to talk to your doctor or consult a sleep specialist. A sleep specialist may recommend a sleep study which, nowadays, with the aid of modern technology, can be done at home. A more in-depth study is typically done at a sleep center.

While your doctor or specialist can help you treat a medical issue preventing you from sleeping, other conditions may require some action on your part at home.

Tips for Better Sleep

You yourself can do many things to help improve your sleep environment. This is also known as sleep hygiene.

Sleep hygiene includes making your bedroom quiet and comfortable. You can close windows and doors to muffle sounds. Using a sleep mask and/or ear plugs or white noise machine can also make your sleep environment more conducive to deep rest.

Keep your room at a comfortable temperature; cooler temperatures aid sleep.

Remember that consistency produces results. Put yourself on a sleep schedule. Going to bed and getting up at the same time each day helps keep your internal clock working properly by aiding your circadian rhythm.

Taking a warm bath before you go to bed or doing restorative yoga or meditation before bed may also help with relaxion. Try doing a meditation that focuses on rest and renewal. Intentional calming before bed can help you to relax and fall asleep more quickly

Avoid drinking caffeine and alcohol or eating big meals before bedtime. Avoid long naps during the day, which can prevent you from falling asleep at your regular time. Try to keep them to 30 minutes maximum.

If your family duties are interfering with sleep, try asking for assistance a few nights per week.

If your concerns and/or to-do list items keep you from falling asleep or wake you up during your sleep, I have found that writing helps. Keep a journal by your bed and write down what's on your mind so that you know it has been identified. Often, the nagging "ghost-worries" haunt our subconscious and keep us up. After I write down what's bothering me, I set an intention of finding a solution at the right time and then let it go for the night. In my experience, this helps to take the "worry weight" off so that I can sleep more peacefully while my subconscious works on the solution. At times, I've actually awoken with a solution!

My views on sleep and its foundational importance for wellness have evolved greatly since doing research for this book.

Not actually knowing *how* I was sleeping became a subject I wished to explore. To that end, I'm now wearing a sleep-tracking device that also monitors my heart rate while asleep as well as my active heart rate during fitness related activities (Withings, n.d.). My main focus, however, is on my nightly sleep information. It's one of the first things I check when I wake up in the morning!

Dialing in Your Best Sleep

Once I put sleep on my priority list, I began to be very conscious of the things that were affecting my sleep. I found that keeping a sleep journal (based on my sleep tracker) by my bed is a helpful tool. In this journal, I note:

- my level of exercise activity that day

- major concerns on my mind

- what I ate and when

- if I drank alcohol and when

I began to see patterns in my daily life. If I had done little exercise or movement, my sleep was less profound.

If I drank alcohol too close to going to bed, I noticed that my sleep was interrupted. Interestingly, I didn't have as much difficulty falling asleep as staying asleep.

If I didn't write down what was bothering me before going to bed, my sleep depth was interrupted.

One thing that has really helped me to sleep is magnesium. I had no idea that magnesium is a mineral that many people are deficient in. Research estimates that most Americans are deficient in this sleep-assisting mineral (Faloon, 2005, Breus, 2017). Magnesium plays a crucial role not only in sleep, but also in our overall wellness (Nutritional Magnesium Association, 2018).

Here are some interesting facts about magnesium:

1. Activates neurotransmitters in your brain that reduce stress and relax muscles.

2. Helps your body transition into a deep state of calm, to fall asleep faster and stay asleep longer.

3. Optimizes sleep cycles by controlling the release of melatonin before and during sleep.

4. Aids neurotransmitters (GABBA receptors) that reduce unwanted nerve movement during the night. (such as what happens in restless leg syndrome).

5. Can help suppress hormone and mood disorders like stress and sadness that inhibit quality sleep.

I use magnesium oil nightly and found it to be a great help for me. I rub it on the inside of my arms before sleeping and it seems to help me to fall asleep and, more importantly, to stay asleep.

Hopefully this information will inspire a renewed interest in your personal sleep process because it's one of *the* most essential parts of our well-being.

CHAPTER 15

COSTA RICA

D id you know that there are five areas in the world that have the highest number of centenarians per capita?

It isn't just their age that's remarkable either. Their vigor and well-being in their years beyond the century mark serve as an example for living at our highest and best self, the best inspiration to model at any age.

In the November 2005 National Geographic magazine cover story "The Secrets of a Long Life," Dan Buettner located and studied the components of the longest living people on the planet. Referred to as Blue Zones, Buettner listed the areas and what common ingredients contribute to the longevity recipe.

One of the five Blue Zone areas is the Nosara Peninsula in Costa Rica.

What are the secrets of the happy and healthy centenarians? With this question in mind, I traveled to Costa Rica where I spent time with Jose, an elder member of the Nosara community. I asked him about their cultural wisdom and point of view on a long and fulfilling life.

Jose was 95. His spirit was bright, his wit was quick, and his smile was ready. He was thin yet strong and moved with grace and ease. Jose was a true charmer, and I was honored to be talking with him.

If the pillars of advice presented to me by Jose sustain and enhance life in the Blue Zones, why not create a foundation for them in our own lives?

The following elements or ingredients for longevity are imbedded in most cultures in varying degrees. However, they're more generally lacking and somehow disassociated from culture in the United States. This may be due, in part, to the "me first," independent, rebellious nature of the nation. And it could be one reason behind the way we reward adversarial, litigious, and competitive behavior.

More people in the USA than in other countries suffer socially, emotionally, psychologically, and spiritually from a lack of connection, compassion, community, and purpose. Not having a sense of belonging can take its toll. Even in nature, different animal species will ban together to help each other in times of hardship. When a shark is threatening a weaker or young member of the pod, Dolphins will swim quickly around the shark to churn the water and disorient their sense of location.

Growing up generally feeling unsupported is quite a challenge to overcome when you don't know what the alternative feels like. This connection to others and purpose, along with a healthy sense of self and laughter, contribute to your overall health and wellness. My wise Uncle Jim told me that "humor helps you to overcome just about everything that ails you."

Family First

"Family first" were the words Jose chose when starting our conversation. We need to band together to support our family members, not to separate and disperse our energy and efforts. Multigenerational living arrangements allow not only for care of the children and the elders but also for the ongoing sharing and learning of perspectives, all in a seamless environment of support.

When we're young, having elders around gives us access to their wisdom, and allows us to observe and learn from their behavior and mistakes. Having young ones around when we're older keeps us hopeful and young at heart. The enthusiasm young people have for life is contagious. Our vitality is automatically renewed at the sight of a little one learning new things, eyes wide with all the wonders and possibilities the world has to offer. Anybody lucky enough to have had a grandmother or grandfather knows how rewarding a bond with an elder can be. It's a secret twinkle, a bond that's profoundly reciprocated and cherished. A loyalty unlike the friendships between other members of the family tribe.

If you don't have close, immediate blood relatives, you can create your own family through true and trusted friendships. I've always believed that "friends are family by choice." Their place in your life reaches beyond

simple consanguinity. Being "like family" is an earned position. I personally have many blood relatives who distance themselves or who are unsupportive in challenging – or sometimes even regular – times.

Standing by you and for you through the seasons of life's trials, successes, and failures, your best friends rise to family status. And you, in turn, do the same. Who could ask for more?

My best friends are truly "soul sisters" and "soul brothers" who are a beautiful and integral part of the tapestry of my life.

Community

Actively participate in community, creating a sense of well-being through having a "tribe" of family, friends, and supporters.

How can you create this? One way could be to volunteer for causes that matter to you. Find activities that align with your values. And, in doing so, you may find a group of people whom you can learn from and feel supported by while contributing to them in the same ways.

Together, as a group, you make a collective contribution to the greater community. It could be serving the homeless in a meaningful way, guiding at-risk teens, or visiting the elderly, for example.

I've found that having a sense of service makes life a little lighter and pays back dividends in knowing that you were able to make a difference. Even with just a little time and energy to put toward the things and people that matter in your community, you initiate a positive ripple effect. If you have a buddy or group with whom to do acts of service, it's even lighter and more rewarding, as you're sharing a common goal. You are, in essence, creating your own tribe.

Downshift (unwind)

Taking a predetermined amount of time away from business and, yes, even electronics is an important element that Jose shared with me. This can help to reduce stress and calm the nervous system, which can, in turn, produce better sleep. A meaningful chat or shared giggles with your loved ones before bed, instead of being glued to your phone or worrying about deadlines, will give everyone a sweet boost of human interaction.

Make a conscious effort to smile each day. We all know how being on the receiving end of one can be uplifting. If you have young children, make it a game to find things to smile about and describe them to one another. Children are naturally looking for the fun in life. As adults, we tend to forget that, as our responsibilities grow and stress creeps into our lives, tightening another notch on our belt.

Schedule a comedy hour regularly, nightly, weekly, or whatever that looks like for you. A movie with the family, comedy club with friends, a home stage-play or puppet show with the kids, charades in the living room with the neighbors. Do anything that tickles your funny bone.

Laughter truly is the music of the soul. Bonding over shared laughter is a wonderful way to connect with your tribe and to promote well-being.

Research has shown that laughter boosts the immune system, which helps you resist illness. It also triggers the release of endorphins, the body's natural feel-good chemical, which promotes an overall sense of well-being (Mayo Clinic, n.d.).

Such powerful health and wellness benefits can be enjoyed every day if you choose.

Find Your Purpose

Why do we get up in the morning? What drives us to do what we do? In our busy, goal-oriented world, sometimes, we lose track of what it's all for in the end. According to the wise Blue Zoner of Costa Rica, knowing what that is, and actively being in alignment with it, can fuel healthy longevity and a sense of well-being.

Jose took great pride in tending the family garden and caring for the grandchildren and great-grandchildren. He was an honored and respected member of the community, which I felt strongly supported his overall health and well-being at the ripe age of 95.

Movement

Consistent natural movement, such as walking, is very important in the longevity equation. Movement produces increased energy and circulation and helps with weight management. No doubt, being active enhances sleep as well. And we know how important sleep is for our well-being.

Movement is another aspect of well-being that children and animals are tuned into naturally. The demands of our adult life as well as our habitual dispositions or tendencies usually contribute to forgetting or ignoring this intrinsic wisdom of the body – or at least letting it fall by the wayside, no longer a priority. But guess what? Lethargy, that nagging feeling you think is in your mind, is actually your body feeling restless and begging you for a little two-step rhythm and blues around the living room or down the street. Your body needs rhythm, to move and express itself. You might consider not taking your dog for a walk as cruel. So why would you be cruel to yourself? We all benefit from fresh air and open space. They engage our senses and clear our mind. Plus, seeking outdoor movement is a great opportunity for (barefoot) grounding.

Sports and body image are more ingrained in some cultures than others, but no matter your culture, movement and physical activity are just as important as proper rest and sleep for overall health.

80% Rule

Were you ever told to "finish your plate?" Eating until we're completely full should never be on the table. Instead, eating until we are 80% full allows our bodies to process and tell us if we require more or not. Typically, it takes 20 minutes to register the feeling of fullness. Eating slowly and mindfully can help give this process the time it needs to promote healthy digestion.

Be mindful, chew your food thoroughly and try putting the fork down between bites.

Jose's family enjoys lively conversation and healthy laughter at meals. Interaction with fellow humans replaces the emphasis of wolfing down what's in front of you so you can get back to the electronics. Although electronics provide immense convenience in communication, they also separate us in so many ways.

The Plant Slant

Eating primarily vegetarian was a point Jose made during our conversation. Meat wasn't vilified; however, most of Jose's daily consumption was from beans, corn, rice, and vegetables. The corn tortillas were made by hand, and the corn was soaked in lime water to release the nutrients. Now that's something you don't see every day.

There is no doubt that healthy, balanced nutrition is a sound practice no matter where you live. Personally, I try to buy organic fruits and vegetables at my local farmer's market whenever possible. Staying away from packaged or canned foods with tons of preservatives in favor of eating fresh and whole foods will jumpstart your wellness journey right now.

So why wait? This is something you can start today.

Faith

Believe in something greater than yourself

As he talked, Jose kept looking upward. Perhaps ancestral guides or spirits were present during our conversation. Maybe my willingness to learn and inquisitiveness intrigued them. Having a spiritual or religious orientation was indicated as an important part of healthy longevity.

This is also the case of the Blue Zone located in Loma Linda, California. Here, the centenarians belong to the faith of Latter-Day Saints. Shared beliefs within the community unify daily activities and support the purpose for which they live.

It doesn't matter what your faith is, or what you believe in. Believing in *something* beyond your current perception and understanding of reality, something greater than yourself, can be truly helpful and uplifting. This is especially true in times of confusion, hardship or when facing the unknown. In times of uncertainty, faith can offer an invisible sense of support. Believing that everything will be all right in the end, or that the universe has your back, can ease the stress and the looming sense of responsibility when you just don't have the answer. There are unseen forces in the universe always working in favor of the greater good. When you pay attention, you'll notice there's always a touch of magic near to ease your mind and heart.

CHAPTER 16

WELL-BEING

> *"Health is a state of complete physical, mental, and social well-being..."* —THE WORLD HEALTH ORGANIZATION

When we talk about well-being, many definitions might come to mind. In conversations with both healthcare professionals and other patients during my travels, the same four components came up again and again: physical, mental, emotional, and spiritual. Most everyone I came across was working on the physical component, as lack of physical well-being can create symptoms that hold us back from quality of life. Physical issues are often most readily identified in the form of pain, limited mobility, high blood pressure, diabetes, or some other traditional medical marker.

However, physical wellness cannot exist in a vacuum, as it is interdependent on the other elements of well-being. For example, when we are worried or stressed, we can feel tired, lethargic, or even sick. This is an example of how mental and/or emotional elements can affect our physical well-being. Being aware of the multiple integrated elements of well-being helps to determine our baseline. And balance in these areas is the key to overall wellness.

Six key factors in well-being have been identified by the Center for Spirituality and Healing at the University of Minnesota: health, environment, community, relationships, security, and purpose. Let's look at each one.

Health includes diet and nutrition, physical activity, sleep, thoughts, emotions and stress mastery.

Environment starts in the home and extends to our planet. Your choices influence the health of your environment and your well-being.

Community includes social connections and networks as well as participation in associations. Community also includes public services, connectedness, equity (basic needs are met) and livability (housing, transportation, parks and recreation, access to culture and the arts).

Relationships include family, friends, and other personal connections that buffer the negative effects of stress and loneliness.

Security consists of taking steps to keep yourself safe, learning to deal with threats and anxiety, and constructing a healthy relationship with money, providing freedom from financial fears.

Purpose is applying your values, passions, and abilities to the benefit of the greater good.

Ultimately, this all starts with a question and comes from within. Ask yourself: What can I do to feel content and balanced? Listen to what your body, mind and spirit are telling you. Be patient with yourself and make sure to celebrate the successes along your journey to well-being.

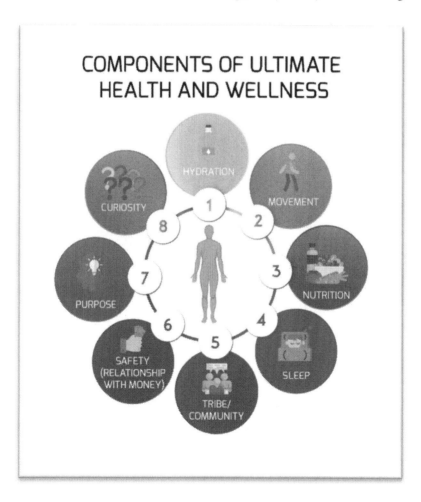

CHAPTER 17

THE ROCKS IN YOUR LIFE JAR

ESTABLISHING PRIORITIES

I magine a big jar. Call it your Life Jar. You're going to fill it up with the components that fill your daily life.

Start with rocks. Rocks, which take up the most space in your life, are those things that are most important to you based on how much time, energy, and consistency you put into them. They could be work, family, friends, travel, and personal or business projects. They also could be things that make you say, "what happened to the day?" In this case, sometimes, rocks sneak their way into your jar without you knowing it, so it's always good to take inventory of the rocks that are in your life jar.

Next, you put pebbles in the jar. These are the things that fill up the space between the rocks; they are part of keeping your life running but less important than the rocks. Pebbles could be shopping, getting gas, personal maintenance, and life planning activities.

Then there's sand. Sand represents the smallest elements that take up the space between rocks and pebbles. Sand consists of those things that aren't necessarily essential to your life but still take time and energy out of your day. Essentially, you wouldn't miss them if they weren't there. Sand could also be sneaky time-wasters that seem to eat at our productivity. No doubt that we all have those in some form or another.

So now I invite you to ask yourself: Are wellness activities or practices rocks, pebbles, or sand in your life jar? For me, wellness practices are a big rock in my life jar, and I have become exceptionally intentional with this because it is immensely important. Even the start-of-flight airline safety briefing tells us: "Put your oxygen mask on first before helping others."

We can't effectively help others around us if we aren't first at our best!

No matter how busy you might be tending to the other "rocks" in your day, your wellness is essential to being able to do so. If you fill your jar with the lesser, unimportant activities (sand and pebbles) there won't be room in your jar to add the rocks.

Adding a personal wellness "rock" to your life jar might involve repositioning some of the other rocks or eliminating sand and pebbles. But this rock will ensure that you're able to continue at your best and highest. You might even need to remove another rock to make room for it as a priority in your jar. The choice is yours.

Remember, when you are at your best and highest, you win and everything and everybody important to you wins as well.

CHAPTER 18

REMEMBER YOUR ABCS

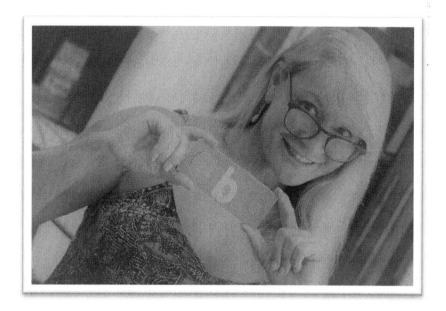

One important thing that I learned through my research is that what we do consistently influences our lives one way or another, like it or not.

If we integrate healthy habits into our lives, the results should speak for themselves. Conversely, if we go down a path that doesn't support our bodies' ability to keep us optimally running, those results will show as well, no matter how hard we may try to cover them up. Sweeping changes in activity or eating aren't always sustainable, and after the wave of enthusiasm wears off, we're left disappointed and deflated.

However, if we take it step by step, slowly incorporating healthy activities, hydration, nutrition, regular sleep, and movement, they can eventually become habits that can ultimately change our lives.

I call it your **ABCs – Always Be Consistent**. Whether it's keeping a container full of water with you to remind you to hydrate throughout the day, a movement, or a meditation practice, consistency is the key to long-term success. Baby steps are still forward motion, and can transition into strides over time.

Part of consistency is to check in with yourself and your body daily. Do you feel dehydrated? Are you feeling tired? Are you sluggish? Your body knows what it needs. Take time to listen and make adjustments as needed.

Chapter 19

Action Plan for Rejuvenating Your Energy on All Levels

Hydration is crucial for keeping all systems of your body operating efficiently. I use a water purifying pitcher. It's important to have back-up filters readily available.

ACTION: Always have (preferably purified) water nearby or in multiple places for easy access. Remember to drink even when you aren't thirsty.

Movement such as walking, stretching, or yoga will keep your metabolism going, your heart strong, and your body in condition.

ACTION: Make a morning ritual of stretching, yoga, or walking. The benefits of morning exercise have been well documented. If you just aren't a morning person, make certain that you set a time for stretching or a walk during the day.

Sleep is fundamental for overall well-being. Not only is the duration of sleep important but also the quality of sleep.

ACTION: Prepare your best sleep environment, which should be cool and dark. Minimize electronics before going to bed. Look into a wearable sleep tracking device to get daily information on your sleep components: duration, depth, regularity, and interruptions.

Earthing has numerous wellness benefits as you discovered in Chapter 9. The good news is that you can start today and right where you are.

ACTION: Connect to the earth in some way every day. If you're fortunate to live in a warmer climate near a lake or the ocean, then walking barefoot near the shoreline is simple and effective. If climate is an issue, I've found that pouring five pounds of Himalayan salt into a bath will provide a similar experience to the natural bathing locations you read about earlier. To make sure you don't have any skin reaction, try immersing your hand in a bowl of warm water with Himalayan salt for 10 minutes and see how it feels. If you feel itchy or develop a rash, try another earthing technique. Working in your garden, either outside or inside can provide earthing benefits as well. Another rather interesting option is to get potting soil or collect dirt from a nonpolluted source outdoors. If the dirt is from outdoors, clean out any rocks, twigs, grass, or debris, and put it in a bowl (probably best in the bathtub or shower). Mix Himalayan salt in warm water and pour over the dirt to make a mud. Put your feet in it for about 20 minutes. If getting wet and/or muddy isn't your thing, investing in an earthing mat or earthing sandals could be the most convenient way to ground.

Nutrition is more than just eating whatever to stop a hunger pang. Hippocrates said: "Let Food Be Your Medicine and Your Medicine be your Food."

ACTION: Clean out your pantry. If it lasts for more than a week, it's covered in preservatives. Forego convenience and, as much as possible, eat whole, organic, plant-based food. Skip the carbonated beverages, packaged or processed pantry-friendly stuff. If it goes bad in three days, you're on the right track.

One caveat is frozen pea protein "burgers" from a company called Beyond Burger. I am crazy about these patties. They're colored with beet juice so they look pink like actual meat. I eat them with sautéed mushrooms and am quite happy to skip beef, chicken, or turkey burgers. They also make a great "meatloaf." Just substitute the patties for regular meat and you have a healthy, plant-based dish that stores well in the fridge for convenience. They also have a sausage version which is also delicious and has a different flavor twist.

Purpose. This is a big one, and the basis for the healthy longevity we see in the Blue Zones.

ACTION: Your purpose lies at the intersection of:

1. What you love. Make a list of those things or activities that inspire and elevate you.

2. What you're good at. Do you have a natural-born talent? What are you complimented for regularly?

3. What the world needs. Can you fill a need with your talents or genius or passion?

4. What you can get paid for. List the ways you can package your talent and skills to be of valuable service.

Relationships are the threads of the fabric of our lives.

ACTION– List the people in your inner circle. They are your time-proven trusted group of supporters. Essentially, they are your "family" – whether by blood or by choice. They are the core of your tribe. What one thing can you do today to nurture those relationships?

Community is your outer circle of friends, neighbors, association members, activity buddies. They are part of your extended tribe.

ACTION– List one thing you'll do this week to enhance your relationship and/or participation with your community.

Safety is more than the absence of being under attack. It's a feeling that you have a soft place to land. This is a natural extension of tribe, yes, but safety can also encompass your relationship with money.

Volumes have been written about this. No matter how much money you may or may not have, until your relationship with money is in balance, your sense of safety will be challenged.

ACTION- Take a close and honest look at your current relationship with money. Write the words: "Money makes me feel_____." Let it flow. I would recommend a quiet and calm place where you can just be without interruption. The most important thing is to be honest. Keep writing as long as you need to. Make certain you write without self-censorship or judgment. This is for your eyes only unless you care to share it. The act of writing what comes up can be very cleansing and initiate a process to continue any clearing that might be needed.

Consistent Curiosity in Life

The beauty of youth is that everything holds a rare and precious discoverability. As time passes, the thrill and wonderment are often replaced with boredom and cynicism. And nothing ages us faster as our loss of enthusiasm for living.

Albert Einstein encourages us to pursue our curiosities. He once said:

"Don't think about why you question, simply don't stop questioning. Don't worry about what you can't answer, and don't try to explain what you can't know. Curiosity is its own reason." Aren't you in awe when you contemplate the mysteries of eternity, of life, of the marvelous structure behind reality? And this is the miracle of the human mind—to use its constructions, concepts, and formulas as tools to explain what man sees, feels and touches. Try to comprehend a little more each day. Looking at life through the eyes of a child keeps things new, fresh, and ever-evolving.

ACTION: Make a list of things that you're curious about. For example, maybe you would like to learn more about our oceans, or scuba diving, or other cultures, or how to fix your car, or why each snowflake is different? The list is endless and there's so much out there to learn. And the more I learn, the more I learn how much more there's to learn! The possibilities and motivations are endless.

CONCLUSION

To explore the facets of your own well-being is a noble quest, one that, no doubt, will lead you on a fascinating journey of consistent discovery and evolution of body, mind, and spirit.

Through all the years of travel that went into researching and immersing myself in ancient and cultural healing practices, I learned one important lesson that has been a game-changer:

Every single day, be in *Gratitude*

Through the lens of Gratitude, things that we would normally take for granted like a roof over our head, clothes on our back, clean water to drink and food on our table become blessings. Living with an "Attitude of Gratitude" changes our perception of life, relationships, events, and the world around us.

Gratitude can also change the way we approach Wellness. I know no other more immediate and profound way to harmonize and rejuvenate body mind and soul than to be in Gratitude daily.

My favorite technique is to write down in a journal for what and for whom I am most grateful. The simple act of thinking about it and writing it down naturally brings us into an energetic field of Gratitude. Add to the journal when things to be grateful for come into focus, no matter how seemingly small. Review it daily. This can be your guide for both creating a daily state of Gratitude in your life, as well as seeing things in a different light. I personally have found the results to be far-reaching and significant. In essence, being in Gratitude has changed the quality of my life.

After all, what could possibly be more valuable than adding profound quality to each blessing-filled year of your life?

To Your Best and Highest,

Kit

Country Descriptions
and Information

BHUTAN

Bhutan is a name neither spoken nor heard by many, yet it is in part thanks to this anonymity that the gorgeous country increasingly inspires such a following. Despite having lived most of its rich history in isolation from the modern world, it merges an incredibly forward-thinking mindset into its traditions. It is, for example, the only country in the world to so value its people's happiness that it actually measures it as a means to judge the country's success. The kingdom calls this Gross National Happiness, as opposed to Gross National Product. A beautiful concept, is it not?

It is a small country, bordering India, Nepal, and Tibet. Bhutan is marked by its Buddhist religion and history of political conflicts, both heavily influenced by its Tibetan neighbor. According to archaeological findings, the area of Bhutan was first settled 4,000 years ago, though most of its earlier history was dominated by warring fiefdoms instead of a single kingdom. It was first unified, with all divisions brought under a central legal code, in the 17th century. After a long period of continued warfare, Bhutan fell under British rule after the Duar War ended in the late 19th century. Nearly 86 years later, after India overthrew British power in 1947, Bhutan finally established its own independent national governing body.

Bhutan maintained the authenticity of its traditional culture by avoiding globalization for most of its history; both political and natural (mountainous) barriers kept foreigners out of the picture. Only in the last 60 years have outsiders been allowed into this Buddhist kingdom, whose isolation has finally begun to give way to a very limited amount of global influence. Today, travelers are still primarily drawn to Bhutan for its beautiful uniqueness; exploring this culture is akin to stepping into another world. As a nation, Bhutan is proud of and committed to upholding its Buddhist culture and traditions. Its national dress, for example, is still donned widely throughout the country and, on certain occasions, mandated. The colors and design indicate citizens' status, a concept still present in this society once based upon a feudal system. Art reflects strongly the beliefs and symbols of its Mahayana Buddhist religion, and sports remain traditional as well, with archery events being some of the most social and competitive functions around the nation.

Colorful and vibrant festivals across Bhutan further enrich the country's unique flavor and enchantment. These festivals, dedicated either to honoring Buddhist traditions or celebrating nature, draw thousands of locals and tourists ever year. Three of the most spectacular festivals are the Paro Tschechu, the Thimpu Tschechu, and the Black-Faced Crane festivals. The first two celebrate Bhutan's Buddhist roots, and include powerful dances, colorful costumes, and intricate face masks as a part of the thousands-strong gathering. The last is a celebration of nature: it marks the arrival of the endangered black-necked cranes to the southern valley of Phobjikha for the winter, honoring them through conservationist-themed music and dancing. Attending any one of Bhutan's many festivals is a once-in-a-lifetime experience, a whirlwind of color, energy, music, food, dancing, and socializing never to be forgotten.

A Buddhist kingdom, with its traditions so well-intact and its foreign influences so limited, Bhutan is an experience beyond what even the seasoned traveler could imagine. It is more than just meeting a new culture or gazing in awe at the staggering mountains that surround it. It is as if one is walking into a glorious past, somehow transported into the modern-era.

GERMANY

It's true; stereotypical images of lederhosen-clad gents, the clinking pints of well-crafted beer, or even particular moments in history are those most likely to spring to mind at the mention of Germany. But to those in the inner circle of health and wellness travel, the mental images conjured instead depict a scene of picturesque healing spas, mineral and thermal springs, and the tranquil forests, rivers, and lakes that set the natural tone for peace and healing. Germany's history of wellness dates back to the early Roman Empire's culture of communal bathing. It further progressed through its own government's 19th century health initiatives and has continued its growth through the centuries, today offering some of the most sophisticated wellness spas in the world.

The name *Germany* is unique from most country names in that it has historically referred more to a group of people than to a specific place. The location and divisions of Germanic peoples have been fluid over the two millennia since their presence in Northern and Western Europe. Even during the great expanse of the Roman Empire, only part of what is now Germany ever fell under Roman authority. However, this part was enough to leave behind great influence. The Romans left a significant mark on Germany's history of health practices, particularly in the area of bathing. Baths were constructed in all territories the Roman Empire occupied, as both physical health centers and as social gathering spaces. The Romans first discovered the hot mineral springs in Germany's city of Baden-Baden and built thermal baths there around 2,000 years ago. Baden-Baden influenced the construction of many baths in its likeness, and thus the Roman bathing culture was planted across Germany.

Long after the decline of the Roman Empire, Germanic political states remained divided until Prussian Prime Minister Otto Von Bismarck merged them to form the German Empire in 1871. Von Bismarck did more than play a key role in Germany's political history; he also set the tone for his citizen's health and wellness practices at the time. All German workers were granted the right to a periodic 4-6 week stay at one of the nation's spas for their physical and mental health. This initiative helped draw attention to Germany's spa culture, helping it become a hub for European wellness travelers in the 19th century.

Despite the trials and tragedies of World Wars I and II, and the aftermath that divided Germany once again, these healing baths and spas survived. In fact, they served as a cultural custom that remained strong in both East and West Germany, linking the divided halves of this nation until they were united at last in 1990. Traditional baths became spas and wellness resorts, incorporating modern practices while maintaining their traditional healing approaches. Health and wellness remain to this day an ingrained part of German culture.

As for other aspects of society, the nation of Germany is a well-rounded reflection of the diversity of its past cultures and political states. Its modern-day religion is a perfect example of this. Historically, both Roman Catholicism and Protestantism gained and lost influence in certain areas, depending on the faith of their state's leader at the time. In present-day German society, these two faiths have roughly equal numbers of followers, both leading the country's religious belief systems. Art, whether visual or written, represents the diverse range of Germanic roots as well; the adjective *Germanic* refers to the cultural identity of the art itself, ignoring the political boundaries of its origin. Globalization has had an enormous effect on Germany; yet much of its contemporary society reflects the general "Western culture" in regard to popular sports, music, film, art, hobbies, and cuisine. Cultural customs such as traditional baths and health centers have not lost their place. Underneath the surface layers of global influences, German cultural identity stands firm, the unmoving foundation of its society even now.

Traditions such as religious feasts and seasonal festivals are still widely celebrated, incorporating authentic customs with modern-day twists. Carnival (Karneval or Fasching depending on the region) is a religious festival with a long history in Germany dating back to the 1200s. Today, it is one of the most spectacular celebrations for Germans and tourists alike to experience. Participants in Karneval can enjoy costume parades, masked dances, energetic people, traditional food, music, drinking, and dancing, all stemming from its Catholic origin of one last, grand celebration before the Lenten season. Oktoberfest, in contrast, is not a religious festival but rather one originating from German history and agriculture. It is a combined celebration of a significant 19th century royal wedding with Munich's agricultural fair. Today the festival is a national holiday, drawing in millions of locals and tourists with its authentic folk songs, costumes, dancing, food, beer, traditional competitions, and even modern-day additions such as roller coasters.

For a country so rarely in its history united as one, Germany maintains impressively intact cultural traditions. Its baths, natural springs, and spas are some of the country's oldest customs, still thriving across the nation today. Throughout all of the tribulations Germany has faced, it has always held close its value of and trust in natural healing. Wellness culture flourishes in contemporary Germany, calling to all travelers who seek to find rest, healing, and peace through a beautiful combination of traditional and modern wellness practices.

COSTA RICA

Pura vida or 'pure life' is the phrase most commonly uttered across Costa Rica, and for good reason. Life in this natural, eco-friendly country embodies just that: purity. Few countries around the world can match its connection to the earth, animals, locally-grown food, natural healing practices, and the environment. Health and wellness fall right within this connection. Costa Ricans truly exemplify the idea of an authentic life, of connecting both to oneself, to others, and to our precious earth through natural practices. The benefits of this harmonious lifestyle are not ambiguous; scientific proof is on Costa Rica's side. It has, for example, been ranked the world's #1 "happiest country" over multiple years, according to the Happy Planet Index. Its Blue Zone on the Nicoya Peninsula is home to some of the oldest and healthiest people across our planet. Costa Rica is rich in the opportunities it provides to all seeking happiness and health through natural processes.

Costa Rican political history is one of overall independence and self-sustainability. In 1821, it officially gained independence from the Spanish Colonial Empire and developed its own political and economic identity soon thereafter. It is, for example, praised as the host of the first free and honest democratic election process in all of Central America, during its 1889 presidential election. The 19th century was also when Costa Rica drew attention and foreign investors thanks to its coffee production, subsequently gaining some economic prosperity. Bananas soon followed coffee as another major world export. Even the country's tangible successes were and are deeply rooted (literally) in the earth and the nature of Costa Rica.

All throughout this history and into today's contemporary Costa Rican society, some factors contributing to their top levels of health and wellness remain unchanged. The Costa Rican lifestyle, especially that practiced in the Blue Zone, centers around a close family and friend community; it promotes a healthy work-social balance; the consumption of natural, locally grown foods; daily movement/activity; a strong faith; and a unique connection to the surrounding natural environment. Costa Rican nature contains 5% of the entire world's biodiversity within its rainforests, jungles, oceans, and diverse plant and animal kingdoms. It is no wonder that it not only creates a welcome environment for its locals but also attracts millions of tourists every year. Costa Rica's harmonious natural atmosphere sets the perfect tone for yoga retreat centers, spas, and wellness resorts that foster peace and health for travelers seeking healing, rest, and a deepened connection to the earth. Hundreds of medicinal herbs grow in the country's rainforests, so natural medicine is also a strong draw for tourists seeking alternative healing practices on their travels.

Certain festivals, both traditional and contemporary, further link residents and tourists to Costa Rica's cultural identity of natural living. A traditional example is the Día de la Virgin del Mar, a festival in July dedicated to honoring the Virgin Mary's protection of the sea and prosperity for the fisherman. The festival is celebrated with intricately decorated boats, Catholic mass, parades, concerts, dances, and even fireworks. A more modern festival, but one still maintaining a strong connection to nature, is Costa Rica's Envision festival every February. It's a gathering of open-minded people that includes activities such as live concerts, yoga on the beachfront, trapeze, dancing, and time to commune with others.

Far too often, we overcomplicate this thing called life. Hungry for success, distracted by advancing technology, isolating ourselves in the name of being independent, feeling like we want to but can't do it all, life can turn into a swirling whirlpool of stress and confusion. But the Costa Ricans have developed a culture whose principles prevent this whirlpool from pulling them in. Their focus on family community, environmental harmony, faith, activity, and natural lifestyles has created a holistic atmosphere in which its citizens thrive, and to which foreigners flock. It's no wonder that their unofficial national slogan is "pura vida." Life in this country is just that: pure.

ITALY

Italy is for romance, for architecture, for dangerously delicious carbohydrates, for ancient history, for gondolas and cappuccinos, and for accordion street music. But it's also for so much more. In focusing so intently on its warm and enticing culture, many tend to overlook Italy's stunning natural geography. Italy's natural resources are due to its unique position that grants access to the northern snowy alps and ski resorts, to the vast green landscapes of Tuscany, and all the way down to its sunny Mediterranean beaches. Indeed, this geography, combined with ancient Roman cultural practices, laid the foundation for Italy's fountain of health and wellness opportunities. Italian earth is alive with natural springs for healing baths and both active and dormant volcanoes that provide mineral-rich mud for different health treatments. Its geographical wonders, mixed with its ancient history, make Italy unique in the world of health and wellness.

The origin of Italian wellness practices is tied to the Roman Empire, and to their devout belief in the natural healing powers of baths. As the Romans expanded their territory, they constructed thermal baths all over, especially where geographical features such as hot or cold mineral springs provided the resources for healing treatments. Romans increasingly expanded the concept of the thermal bath beyond just the act of bathing and water health therapies; soon, they included massage rooms, saunas, and even recovery rooms for wounded soldiers. Although the overall focus remained on health, they also developed into social and community centers, some even growing to contain sport areas, gardens, libraries, and meeting spaces to commune and hold discussions.

Throughout its political trials, divisions, wars, and advancements, there were times when the Italian culture lost the closeness of its connection to these bathing centers. For example, World Wars I and II contributed to the destruction of some of these ancient baths, and the aftermath of the overall post-war economic decline distracted many from what had previously been such a foundational part of Italian life. However, these periods always passed. Eventually, Italy always returned to welcome baths and wellness centers back as an essential part of its culture. With renewed time and resources dedicated to the study of the healing properties of bathing, hydrology, and thermal cures in the late 20th century, Italy's contemporary focus on the benefits of wellness spas has been fully revived.

Ranking 10th in the world for its wellness tourism market, Italy offers some of the most spectacular healing spas and resorts, with some of the most authentic and ancient history behind them. Beyond the modern-day continued practice of bathing culture, Italy's present society still incorporates other elements of the ancient baths' extended functions. Italian youth are more likely than many of their generational counterparts across the Western world to meet in person, even though they have access to the same technology and global influences as the others. The cultural practice of a meeting space, of communal time shared in person, remains securely downloaded on the hard drive of each Italian citizen, passed down from their ancient Roman ancestors. So, whether for the medicinal advantages of its exquisite and historic spas, or for the emotional health and wellness benefits of true connection to others, Italy calls to all travelers seeking healing and rest of all kinds.

USA

A single country as large as a continent, the vast diversity found within the United States of America makes any attempt to summarize its cultural identity no small feat. True to the myriad of cultures that live within our country borders, the concept of health and wellness across the United States is also so varied that it essentially reflects the entire world's beliefs and practices. As we know, the U.S. is one of the world's leading nations to have most recently received European settlers. The consequence of this relatively short, post colonization history is that many of our modern society's cultural practices are not originally our own, but rather are adopted from previous civilizations or from immigrant populations. It is the combination of these adopted practices, intertwining and further developing, that bond together to create the culture that makes the USA us.

Wellness, as a modern term, is one concept that did rise specifically out of the melting pot of ideas, backgrounds, and beliefs called the United States. Though the roots underneath the concept are ancient, our contemporary use of the term *wellness* was first developed in 1950s USA. Doctors in the 50s-70s observed that most diseases killing Americans were now a result of lifestyle and behavior, rather than uncontained viruses. They were preventable, at least in theory, if one were only to live a healthier lifestyle. This became the initial concept of wellness: the idea of promoting physical, mental, and emotional health as prevention to sickness, instead of focusing healthcare solely upon medical cures. It then developed further into the belief that the purpose of wellness was not just to avoid disease or illness but, rather, to truly live a happy, balanced, healthy, quality life. The idea was adopted and promoted by the World Health Organization and has influenced not only the world of medicine and healthcare but also government, business, and the tourism industry.

Sleep health has been considered a part of wellness since its origin, but only over the last few decades has it gradually stepped into the spotlight as a vital component of overall health. In our 21st century world, sleep, all too often, takes a back seat to the demands of work and pressures of success in all areas of life. The United States has been a pioneer in the science of sleep, researching its properties, necessities, and health functions. Strangely enough, our global culture almost praises lack of sleep, as if sleeping less than necessary means one is sacrificing it for the greater good of career success or family. The dangers of too little sleep, however, are both daunting and proven. The data details the detrimental issues that arise in the health of the individual, and beyond this, even in the areas of production in the workforce or in the millions of dollars allocated to sleep-related illness and accidents every year.

Sleep, as a part of the overall wellness culture in the United States, is finally being recognized for the essential role it plays in not only individual health but also in that of the greater society. With an estimated 50-70 million Americans struggling with chronic sleep problems, sleep research centers have arisen in response. These centers take a clinical approach, studying the patients' sleep patterns and issues to provide recommended solutions. For those seeking not a clinic but, rather, a wellness getaway with a focus on deep, sound rest, sleep spas across the U.S. will welcome you with open arms and a comfortable pillow. Combining ancient concepts of massage, aromatherapy, and essential oils with contemporary natural techniques to calm the body into a state of deep rest, these spas offer a place to rejuvenate through sleep.

The United States, so "new" in its phase as a modern, cosmopolitan society, has still managed to emerge as a world leader in the field of wellness. Its hurried culture, in which success is the destination and stress seems to be the path leading to it, has birthed a movement of wellness counteracting this "eye on the prize" culture with the promotion of rest, rejuvenation, self-care, overall health, and happiness. An old Irish proverb advises that "a good laugh and a long sleep are the two best cures for anything." Wellness would likely agree but add that they're not only cures but also essential foundational blocks on which to build a healthy and joyful life.

THAILAND

Thailand is a country of enduring independence and strong cultural traditions. Formerly Siam, the kingdom of Thailand remains, to this day, the only country in Southeast Asia to never have been ruled by Western colonists. Present-day Thailand isn't best known for its political resilience, however, but rather for the constant stream of travelers who flock to it for the unique experience of Thai food, nature, traditional customs, animal sanctuaries, and religion, all for an unbelievably low cost. But this one-of-20-most-visited-countries also has ancient medicine and healing practices to draw in anyone looking to spend some quality time on their health and wellness. Thai healing is a balanced combination of herbalism, massage, and meditation. The ultimate goal of these wellness practices is to align the body, mind, and soul in agreement.

Traditional Thai Medicine developed with heavy influences from its surrounding countries. Thailand's proximity to both India and China meant that its healing techniques were influenced by yoga, Ayurveda, and Traditional Chinese Medicine. The Thai foundational elements of earth, wind, water, and fire were over the years embellished and developed by visitors and immigrants from surrounding countries. Thailand began to integrate ideas and practices from the traditional medical cultures of India and China into its own, eventually becoming the holistic Traditional Thai Medicine that we still see today.

Thai massage is a healing and relaxation art form renowned worldwide. It goes back 2,500 years when the expansion of Buddhism across India and Southeast Asia brought a mixture of healing techniques together. In fact, Thai massage is so linked to Buddhism that for many centuries, only monks were able to practice it, and only in monasteries that doubled as medical centers. To this day, although the tradition has eased and most modern-day practitioners are no longer monks, the masseur should still customarily say a prayer before beginning the Thai massage. The foundation of Thai massage is its system of therapy points along the human body, diagrammed over 2,000 years ago. The belief is that if these therapy points are imbalanced, the body is susceptible to disease and fatigue. By correctly massaging these points and balancing the body's energy, illnesses can be cured and pain eradicated. Herbal remedies are also used in Traditional Thai Medicine; menthol and camphor (two main ingredients in Tiger Balm) are often utilized in Thai herbalism to ease pain. Lavender oil is used to calm nerves and refresh the mind. Meditation is a staple not only of Thai medicine, but of the Buddhist religion to which it is so deeply linked. This is considered the final essential piece of the mind-body accord puzzle, one must seek healing treatments not only for the body but also for the mind.

Though it has always been relatively separate from the Western world, given its political independence, certain elements of Thai culture have reached contemporary Western society and influenced it. Thai massage is one example; it has taken off in popularity and has traveled far and wide beyond its country of origin. The massage style has so greatly influenced the Western world that nearly every U.S. or European spa includes Thai massages on their menu. As we know, Thailand's allure as a travel destination has also captivated the West. Elephant sanctuaries, tuk tuk (three-wheeled taxi) rides, delicious and traditional food, and particular festivals are just some of the cultural experiences that catch the tourist's eye. The Yi Peng Floating Lantern Festival is a specific example; drawing tens of thousands of locals and tourists every year, this festival is held on the twelfth full moon of the year and stems from the Buddhist religion. The act of releasing the lanterns into the sky is seen as sending off any ill will or bad experiences from the past year and is done in conjunction with making a positive wish to carry into the new year. Pretty in line with overall mind, body, soul health, don't you think?

Wellness in Thailand is holistic and complete. It's the fusion of herbal treatments, traditional Thai massage, and meditation. Just like the belief that Thai massage brings a balance of energy to one's body, when the three elements of Traditional Thai Medicine combine, it is believed that they bring balance to not only the body but also the soul and entirety of self. So, come to Thailand, and come hungry. Feed your stomach with authentic food, your sense of adventure with endless cultural experiences, and your body and soul with holistic and traditional Thai wellness practices. You will leave well-fed, body, mind, soul, and spirit.

BULGARIA

Every so often, we find what we are searching for in the least expected places. Bulgaria is a living example of this. In a country that has been long-affected by post-World War II communism and economic depression, it contains within its borders some of the richest resources for spiritual healing and wellness to be found across the world. From healing sites, to folk traditions, to religious temples, to mineral springs, Bulgaria is today known as the host of some of the most exquisite spas and most visited healing sites in the world.

Bulgaria's history dates back to some of the earliest sophisticated civilizations recorded. Its city of Plovdiv is considered "Europe's Oldest City" and still today contains remnants of all the impressive cultures that once inhabited it. Containing ancient pottery and jewelry dating to 5000 BC (some of the first produced in the world), a Roman colosseum, medieval and ornate Orthodox churches, and Turkish coffee houses from the Ottoman Empire, Bulgaria is a living representation of its own history, ancient through contemporary.

Influenced by each of these inhabitants over its long and storied history is Bulgaria's culture of health and wellness. Spa culture in Bulgaria is exceptionally developed; its plethora of mineral springs has laid the foundation for the construction of so many high-quality spas, offering a variety of healing treatments, that no matter where you are in Bulgaria you will find one within reach. For travelers seeking an experience more on the spiritual side of wellness, Bulgaria is simply a treasure chest waiting to be opened. The country boasts numerous spiritual sites, from monasteries to mosques, and even temples dedicated to the small religious minority of Buddhists in Bulgaria. Energy of past spiritual events is said to be alive throughout Bulgaria, like that within the caves of the Rhodope Mountains in which the ancient god Orpheus is said to have been. Perhaps its most visited spiritual sites, however, are those less tied to specific religions and more open to general spiritual practitioners seeking peace and healing. Demir Baba Teke is one such site; it is the mausoleum of 16th century Alevist healer Demir Baba and is believed to hold healing energy for those seeking it. The practice is to hang a piece of cloth on a tree near the mausoleum, with the faith that the sickness of one's body will remain on the tree while he who hung it walks away healed.

Even more popular is the Seven Rila Lakes on Rila Mountain. A spiritual group called the White Brotherhood, widely popular in

Bulgaria, uses this place for their yearly spiritual gatherings. The White Brotherhood, founded by the mystic Peter Deunov, is known as a sort of esoteric style of Christianity, focusing on the honor of the body, spirit, and universe. These yearly gatherings reenact their traditional Paneurhythmy dance, set to music that creates an almost trance-like effect to welcome in their new religious year by reconnecting to the universe.

Perhaps, to many, an unlikely place for a spiritual awakening, Bulgaria confidently demonstrates its healing bounty all the same. Its history reads like a fascinating novel of spiritual development through the influences of its myriad of diverse cultural inhabitants over the centuries. Religious diversity is alive and well in Bulgaria, but so is a more general spirituality connected to wellness and healing. A journey to Bulgaria is a journey for your mind, body, and spiritual being. A journey to authentic healing, in all senses of the word.

ROMANIA

Romania has spent the chief part of its modern history under the control of outside rulers. The Romans, various nomadic tribes, Hungarians, Turks, and Russians all did their best to permanently annex Romanian land and assimilate its people to their own societies. But beneath the changing rulers, governments, territorial boundaries, and laws, Romania's true treasure remained firm underground: its natural resources. With nearly two thirds of all of Europe's mineral water springs coursing through its land, Romania has an abundance of earth's most precious resource living underfoot. This plethora of healing springs has always connected the Romanian people to the vitality of nature and has been the foundation for their traditional wellness treatments for thousands of years.

Romania may not be known for luxury travel or picturesque beach vacations, but every year, its recognition for its traditional healing treatments and expanding spa culture is earning it an important spot on the wellness tourism map. Romanian traditional health practices are based upon the nature with which they have always interacted. One spa owner describes how nature teaches us the importance of the seasons to regenerate the environment, and how our human bodies need these natural cycles of healing treatments to regenerate itself as well. As with many of the countries we've been studying, Romanian culture itself has embraced and lived these beliefs for thousands of years; however, only in the last few decades have they been specifically creating spas and resorts to target foreigners to participate in their health culture.

Romanian spas today include a myriad of treatments, all established based on their firm foundation of ancient Romanian traditions. Many utilize products only found locally from their own earth. Pharmaceutical treatments are based solely on plants grown in Romania, like basil and geranium; the healing and thermal water treatments deploy Romanian mineral water; the mud treatments contain the minerals and vitamins from Romanian earth; and so on. Even healing rituals contain processes or names that relate to the country's culture and history. For example, the Queen Marie Ritual of Romania's Tisa Resort is an aromatherapy treatment used with extract of violet, the perfume for which their beloved previous queen is known. Health treatments found at these spas range in function and in intensity, with some purported to heal diseases and disorders of the lungs, nervous system, heart, and more, and others having the goal of simply inducing relaxation and rejuvenation for the mind and body. No matter the treatments sought at any of Romania's 80+ spas, one thing is for certain: you'll experience holistic wellness like never before.

Romanian health culture is not only limited to spa centers. Lake Techirghiol is known around the world for its healing mud and waters. The healing site's legend is one of a crippled old man, named Tekir, and his donkey. The story goes that the man accidentally came upon the lake and upon trying to backtrack, his donkey simply refused to budge. Both man and donkey were stuck in the mud for hours as the man tried to pull his donkey to shore. When they finally broke free, the man realized that his once-blind eyes could now see, and his once-crippled legs could now walk. Ever since, both locals and foreigners have traveled to the lake to bathe in its water and mud for their healing powers. So, whether searching for healing in natural spa treatments, or in the mud and waters of nature itself, Romania offers countless sites in which to find healing and peace.

While for so long in the U.S., the word *spa* has been associated with the idea of pampering or luxury, in Romania, it's rather accepted as an integral and regular practice for one's overall health. Traditional Romanian healthcare encourages the idea of caring for oneself, both body and mind, before any issue may arise, instead of only in response to it. It reminds us that nature maintains its health through cycles and seasons of rituals and regeneration, and that our body craves the same level of care, that our wellness demands to be prioritized and maintained, like the ancient Romanians believed. And what better place to seek out this care than in Romania, home to some of the most mineral-rich natural water in the entire world?

SRI LANKA

The level of wellness and harmony that many of us attain only on getaway trips is simply the authentic way that Sri Lankans live life. Thousands of years before *wellness* was ever tagged as a buzzword, Sri Lanka had already been living out the concept's main principles through its own traditional health practices. Unlike much of Western medicine, Sri Lankan healthcare does not disassociate physical from mental and emotional health; all facets of care for the body and mind are considered within this system. Its attraction as a wellness escape destination is furthered by its stunning natural beauty. Its sun, beaches, and mountains set the tone for comprehensive peace of mind, body, and soul.

As with every country, Sri Lanka's political and economic history has influenced its health culture. Ancient legends detail Sri Lankan healthcare dating back 5,000 years. It has even been credited as the first country in the world to establish and build hospitals as early as the fourth century BCE. The traditional knowledge of health and medicine that Sri Lanka possesses was greatly influenced by the East-to-West silk route. Situated strategically along the route, Sri Lanka gained influential knowledge and cultural practices from African, Middle Eastern, and Eastern countries. India, specifically, contributed greatly to the Sri Lankan health system with the Ayurveda teachings and practices. Sri Lanka's geographic position allowed it the best of both worlds; it could benefit from these outside influences through its location along the trading route, but simultaneously maintain its authenticity thanks to its island structure that provided isolation from excessive globalization.

Even during its many years under the colonial rule of the Portuguese, Dutch, and British, Sri Lanka's island shape and strength of traditions protected it from ever assimilating entirely into the European cultures.

Sri Lankan traditional medicine was and is centered on the concept of Ayurveda, now recognized by the World Health Organization as a holistic natural healthcare system. Ayurveda's foundational principle teaches that the mind has significant influence over the body. This belief has been the guiding force in the development of the different practices and treatments used in Sri Lanka's health system to this day. Medical treatments include acupuncture, homeopathy, alchemical fusion treatments for all diseases (called Rasa Shastra), and many different types of indigenous practices. The system also features both preventative and curative mental health practices like meditation, Buddhist chanting/recitation called pirith, participation in both religious and nonreligious rituals, healing through prayers and spirits, the use of amulets, palm reading, and more. Fused together, all these treatments represent Sri Lanka's holistic and comprehensive approach to traditional healthcare for the mind, body, and spirit.

Though the average tourist planning a trip to Sri Lanka still does so more to enjoy its natural tranquility, gorgeous views, and diverse culture, wellness tourism is catching up in popularity. In fact, so much of the Sri Lankan culture points toward its traditional health practices that even traveling to the country solely for tourism or culture can often turn into a wellness trip by the end. The natural, healthy food, the heightened spiritual presence of Buddhist, Hindu, and Muslim faiths, and the cultural festivals that incorporate rituals used as part of Ayurveda healthcare provoke an authentic feeling of connectedness to one's overall wellness. Take the Esala Perahera festival, for example. It's famous worldwide for its vibrant colors and spectacular parades of dancers, acrobats, and ceremonially-dressed elephants. Underneath all the beauty and dazzle, however, is an even more important reason to participate in this festival: the spiritual awakening that it honors, recognizing Buddha's first sermon there.

One of the most profound elements of Sri Lanka's modern wellness culture is how absolutely authentic it is. There is no show put on for tourists, no construction of random spas simply to draw in more travelers, no attempt to create a wellness culture to follow the tourism trends of modern times. It's simply a country full of people living a lifestyle of holistic wellness and opening the door of hospitality to all who seek to benefit from the same traditions that the Sri Lankans themselves have for 5,000 years.

CHINA

Both one of the world's most ancient sophisticated cultures, and one of its contemporary superpowers, China's historical path from the first to the latter is undeniably fascinating and complex. It is no secret that the Chinese consider their traditions sacred to their cultural identity. Whether festivals, food, or customs, the significance that the Chinese place upon their traditions has long ensured the maintenance of their authenticity, even into present day society. The honored reputation of Traditional Chinese Medicine (TCM) is known in all corners of the world and is held close to Chinese cultural identity. Hardly any nation or individual in our modern world could claim to be unaware or uninfluenced by TCM, even if they themselves are not patients of this treatment system. Acupuncture, tai chi, herbal medicine, and more, have all evolved out of China's traditional set of beliefs regarding holistic, comprehensive health.

Originating somewhere between 4,000 and 5,000 years ago, Traditional Chinese Medicine has its roots both in Taoism and in Buddhism. It was never limited solely to the physical health of the body, but rather has incorporated all facets of health into a holistic wellness approach since its birth. The traditional techniques utilized in this approach stem from certain core beliefs. One such belief is in Qi, the energy that TCM believes flows through all bodies, performing significant functions to maintain health. Another is the concept of yin and yang, two opposing yet balancing energetic forces that, when in harmony, promote peace and health, and when imbalanced, cause disease and harm. Thus, built upon the foundation of beliefs such as these, Traditional Chinese Medicine developed treatments that work to balance the body's energy, control, and harmony.

Tai chi, acupuncture, and herbal medicine are the three practices of Traditional Chinese Medicine that have become most popular in the United States. Tai chi, a body movement practice that focuses on breathing and control to unite the body and mind, can be observed in many outdoor parks and town squares across the U.S., especially during the morning hours. Forty-five U.S. states now hold acupuncture licenses to help patients relieve pain or stimulate relaxation through this approach of penetrating the skin at specific pressure points with small metal needles. Chinese herbal medicine utilizes different plants, vitamins, and minerals to treat a multitude of conditions, and is used by many Americans both instead of and in addition to Western medicine approaches. Beyond these three most globalized techniques, TCM also utilizes Chinese massage (tui na), dietary programs, moxibustion (applying heat directly above acupuncture points), and more. These authentic and traditional approaches to holistic health are available to any visitor of China's tens of thousands of hospitals, clinics, and wellness resorts dedicated to the practice of TCM.

Elements of Traditional Chinese Medicine can be seen in countless cultural customs and festivals across China. For example, the region of Yunnan hosts the Snow Mountain Retreat, an event that draws wellness travelers from all over the world. This retreat focuses on health through detox, including activities like meditation, yoga, tea drinking, and raw food eating. Another example is China's own IWF Shanghai, a fitness trading festival and competition. Of rising importance in China's modern health culture is the focus on physical fitness. Natural exercise and a healthy diet have always been essential to Traditional Chinese Medicine's holistic view of health, but recently the concept of physical health has been taken to new heights. IWF Shanghai is a fitness event and competition held annually that has drawn nearly 50,000 visitors in recent years.

No matter one's views on China as a rising superpower in the modern world, we can all agree that its ancient medical practices and holistically developed health system are quite impressive. Their influence on the international medical community is undeniable. Both the core beliefs of Traditional Chinese Medicine and its many healing techniques are practiced and honored worldwide. Though most of us could find a TCM practitioner close to home, nothing can quite compare to traveling to the birthplace of these natural healing techniques and receiving them surrounded by and immersed in their authentic culture. Wellness is woven into and throughout China's entire culture. From its history to its healthy food to its focus on nature, exercise, mindfulness, celebrations, festivals, religion, and the search for balance in all things, Chinese wellness practices have withstood the test of time.

HUNGARY

A common theme among many of the countries we're studying is the presence of geothermal springs and their influence on the wellness practices of those cultures. Hungary takes this to the next level. Unparalleled in its thermal and mineral water coverage, nearly the entire country has healing springs bubbling below the surface at temperatures of 45 to 100 degrees Celsius (113 to 212 degrees Fahrenheit). In fact, Hungary's land contains 147 different types of qualified medical water (mineral water that has been demonstrated to have healing effects through medical testing). It's no wonder that its traditional healing practices mostly originate in thermal and mineral water treatments, though its modern spas and wellness centers also incorporate a variety of diverse health treatment options as well.

Over the course of Hungary's history, its foreign inhabitants have all been influenced by the country's hot springs. In return, they have left their own mark upon the springs, building baths and spas over and near many of these therapeutic water sources. In simply enjoying Hungary's wellness culture, one can figuratively travel through time, stopping at ancient Roman spas, Turkish baths, and the different modern spa types in existence today, ranging from medicinal healing resorts to party spas. Water treatments are far broader and more diverse than simply baths or pools; Hungarians utilize several traditional, healing practices in partnering with their thermal water supply. Some such treatments include: aqua therapy, saunas, steam baths, aroma cabins, bath meditation, and more. These techniques can be used as medical treatment for countless diseases and conditions, or also simply to relax and rejuvenate a mind and body in need of rest. Perhaps one of the most beautiful qualities of Hungarian spas is that they're open to the public and can be accessed for day use at affordable prices. Thus, health and wellness are not reserved for the wealthy here; they are for locals and travelers alike, anyone seeking the peace and healing that awaits them in the minerals of Hungarian waters.

Culture, history, nature, and folk traditions provide ample additional draw for tourists to plan a trip to Hungary even outside of wellness purposes. Hungary provides a scenic backdrop of staggering mountains, rolling sand hills, and the gorgeous Danube river. Its different regions carry on their traditional cultures with pride even today. More rural areas still practice traditional farming techniques and demonstrate a past way of life to tourists through horse shows and festivals. Other regions house historical and natural sites; the Caves of Aggtelek, in which Neolithic and Paleolithic artifacts were found, was proclaimed an UNESCO World Heritage site. Still others contain baroque-style castles or cultural festivals that attract all seeking to experience the fascinating history of Hungary in addition to its healing waters.

There's no debate regarding Hungary's rich supply of healing natural resources; of all countries in the world, it ranks fifth in its underground stock of thermal and mineral springs. The healing properties flowing within these waters are proven and powerful. The body and soul can truly rest in this country that's wealthy not only in terms of its geothermal bounty but also in its unique and traditional culture. A wellness journey to Hungary will fill you with a sense of history, authenticity, peace, and bodily rejuvenation and healing.

Resource List

A Brief History of Wellness: http://www.mywellnesstest.com/certResFile/BriefHistoryofWellness.pdf

Barefoot Parks: https://together-magazine.com/magazine/33-community/191-barefoot-parks

Barefoot Parks: https://www.footfiles.com/subject/barefoot-parks

Healthy China: 5 Wellness Destinations in the People's Republic: https://gbtimes.com/healthy-china-5-wellness-destinations-peoples-republic

History of Ayurveda Natural Medicine in Sri Lanka: http://thespicejournal.com/natural-medicines/history/

History of Wellness: https://globalwellnessinstitute.org/industry-research/history-of-wellness/

IWF: Health, Wellness, Fitness Expo: http://www.ciwf.com.cn/en/

The Healing Power of the Breath: Simple Techniques to Reduce Stress and Anxiety, Enhance Concentration, and Balance Your Emotions, https://coherentbreathing.org/

The Promise of SLEEP. William Dement & Christopher Vaughan: https://www.penguinrandomhouse.com/books/39377/the-promise-of-sleep-by-william-c-dement-md-phd-and-christopher-vaughan/9780440509011/

Traditional Chinese Medicine: In Depth: https://nccih.nih.gov/health/whatiscam/chinesemed.htm

References

Bai, Z., Chang, J., Chen, C., Li, P., Yang, K., & Chi, I. (2015). Investigating the effect of transcendental meditation on blood pressure: a systematic review and meta-analysis. *Journal of Human Hypertension, 29*(11), 653-662. Retrieved from https://www.ncbi.nlm.nih.gov/pubmed/25673114

Bauer, B. A. (2017, June 17). What is an infrared sauna? Does it have health benefits? *Healthy Lifestyle.* Retrieved from https://www.mayoclinic.org/healthy-lifestyle/consumer-health/expert-answers/infrared-sauna/faq-20057954

Béni, A. (2017, May 3). The history of Hungarian thermal baths and bathing culture. *Daily News Hungary.* Retrieved from https://dailynewshungary.com/history-hungarian-thermal-baths-bathing-culture/

Breus, M. (2017, November 20). Magnesium – How it affects your sleep [blog post]. Retrieved from https://thesleepdoctor.com/2017/11/20/magnesium-effects-sleep/

Centro Studi Termali Pietro D'Abano. (n.d.). Retrieved from http://www.centrostuditermali.org/

Chevalier, G., Sinatra, S. T., Oschman, J. L., Sokal, K., & Sokal, P. (2012). *Journal of Environmental Health and Policy.* Retrieved from http://www.hindawi.com/journals/jeph/2012/291541/

Dalton, S. (2018). Breathe deeper to improve health and posture. Healthline Newsletter. Retrieved from https://www.healthline.com/health/breathe-deeper-improve-health-and-posture

Earthing. (n.d.). Retrieved from https://www.earthing.com/

Faloon, W. (2005, September). How many Americans are magnesium deficient? *Life Extensions Magazine.* Retrieved from https://www.lifeextension.com/magazine/2005/9/awsi/Page-01

Finkel, M. (2018, August). While we sleep, our mind goes on an amazing journey. *National Geographic Magazine.* Retrieved from https://www.nationalgeographic.com/magazine/2018/08/science-of-sleep/

Finnleo. (n.d.). Health benefits of sauna. Retrieved from https://www.finnleo.com/pages/health-and-wellness

Goldsby, T. L. et al. (2016). Effects of singing bowl sound meditation on mood, tension, and well-being: An observational study. *Journal of Evidence-Based Integrative Medicine, 22*(3), 401-406. Retrieved from https://journals.sagepub.com/doi/full/10.1177/2156587216668109

Health benefits of acupuncture. (n.d.). Retrieved from http://www.acupuncture-treatment.com/treatment-benefits/

James Oschman. (n.d.). Retrieved from https://www.energy-medicine.org/james-oschman.html

Jennings, K-A. (2017, July 31). Fifteen natural ways to lower your blood pressure. *Medical News Today.* Retrieved from https://www.medicalnewstoday.com/articles/318716.php

Koike M. K., & Cardoso R. (2014). Meditation can produce beneficial effects to prevent cardiovascular disease. *Hormone Molecular Biology and*

Clinical Investigation. 18(3), 137–143. Retrieved from
https://www.ncbi.nlm.nih.gov/pubmed/25390009

Laukkanen, T., Kunutsor, S., Kauhanen, J., & Laukkanen, J. A. (2017).
Sauna bathing is inversely associated with dementia and Alzheimer's
disease in middle-aged Finnish men. *Age and Ageing, 46*(2), 245–
249. Retrieved from
https://academic.oup.com/ageing/article/46/2/245/2654230

MacKinnon, M. (2016). The science of slow deep breathing.
Psychology Today. Retrieved from
https://www.psychologytoday.com/us/blog/neuraptitude/201602/the-
science-slow-deep-breathing

Masakazu, I. et al. (2001). Repeated thermal therapy improves impaired
vascular endothelial function in patients with coronary risk factors.
Journal of the American College of Cardiology, 38(4), 1083-
1088. Retrieved from
https://www.sciencedirect.com/science/article/pii/S073510970101467X

Masala, D., & Merolle, V. (2017). *Senses & Sciences, 4*(2), 365-
370. Retrieved from
https://www.researchgate.net/publication/317503571_The_tuning_fork
_and_the_Soundtherapy

Mason, B. A. (2017, December 11). How negative ions produce positive
vibes *Huffington Post.* Retrieved from
https://www.huffingtonpost.com/entry/how-negative-ions-produce-
positive-vibes_us_5a2eca7fe4b00be52e9d4ae2

Mayo Clinic. (n.d.). Stress relief from laughter? It's no joke. *Healthy Lifestyle*. Retrieved from https://www.mayoclinic.org/healthy-lifestyle/stress-management/in-depth/stress-relief/art-20044456

Mays, L. W. (2018). Ancient water technologies. Retrieved from https://ancientwatertechnologies.com/

McKinney, C. H., & Honig, T. J. (2017). Health outcomes of a series of bonny method of guided imagery and music sessions: A systematic review. *Journal of Music Therapy, 54*(1), 1–34. Retrieved from https://academic.oup.com/jmt/article-abstract/54/1/1/2646241?redirectedFrom=fulltext

Neikrug, A. B., & Ancoli-Israel, S. (2009), Sleep disorders in the older adult – A mini-review. *Gerontology, 56*(2), 181–189. Retrieved from https://www.researchgate.net/profile/Sonia_Ancoli-Israel

Nutritional Magnesium Association, (2018). Magnesium – The Missing Link to Total Health – Radio Interview. Retrieved from http://www.nutritionalmagnesium.org/magnesium-the-missing-link-to-total-health-radio-interview

Ober, C. (2014), *Earthing: The most important health discovery ever!* Laguna Beach, CA: Basic Health Publications

Oschman, J. (2000). *Energy medicine: The scientific basis*. London, England: Churchill Livingstone.

Quach, J., & Lee, J. A. (2017). Do music therapies reduce depressive symptoms and improve QOL in older adults with chronic disease? *Nursing. 47*(6), 58–63. Retrieved from https://journals.lww.com/nursing/Fulltext/2017/06000/Do_music_therapies_reduce_depressive_symptoms_and.17.aspx

Russell, A. (2006). The potential of regenerative medicine [video]. Retrieved from https://www.ted.com/talks/alan_russell_on_regenerating_our_bodies/transcript

Sanatoriul Balnear se de Recuperare Techirghiol (n.d.) About us. Retrieved from https://sbtghiol.ro/en/acasa/about-us/

Surging Life. (n.d.). Ha breathing technique ha the Huna breath of life infuse with energy. Retrieved from https://surginglife.com/ha-breathing-technique-ha-the-huna-breath-of-life-infuse-with-energy/

Techirghiol Primaria Orașului (2011). Overview. Retrieved from http://www.primariatechirghiol.ro/home/info-turism/travel-information/overview/

Thorpe, M. (2017). 12 science-based benefits of meditation. Healthline Newsletter. Retrieved from https://www.healthline.com/nutrition/12-benefits-of-meditation

Withings. (n.d.). Sleep tracking mat. Retrieved from https://www.withings.com/us/en/sleep

Manufactured by Amazon.ca
Bolton, ON